Homework Helpers

Eureka Math
Grade 5

Special thanks go to the Gordan A. Cain Center and to the Department of Mathematics at Louisiana State University for their support in the development of *Eureka Math*.

Book 6

Homework Helpers

Grade 5
Module 1

G5-M1-Lesson 1

Note: It is common to encourage students to simply "move the decimal point" a number of places when multiplying or dividing by powers of 10. Instead, encourage students to understand that the decimal point lives between the ones place and the tenths place. The decimal point does not move. Rather, the digits shift along the place value chart when multiplying and dividing by powers of ten.

Use the place value chart and arrows to show how the value of the each digit changes.

1. $4.215 \times 10 = 42.15$

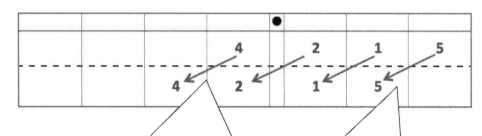

4 ones times 10 is 4 tens. Since I'm multiplying by 10, the value of each digit becomes 10 times greater.

When multiplying by 10, each digit shifts 1 place to the *left* on the place value chart.

2. $421 \div 100 = 4.21$

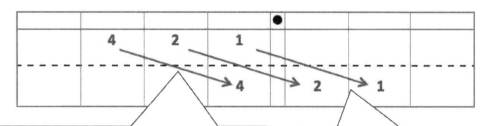

4 hundreds divided by 100 is 4 ones. Since I'm dividing by 100, the value of each digit becomes 100 times smaller.

When dividing by 100, each digit shifts 2 places to the *right* on the place value chart.

EUREKA MATH   Lesson 1:   Reason concretely and pictorially using place value understanding to relate adjacent base ten units from millions to thousandths.   1

©2015 Great Minds. eureka-math.org
G5-M1-HWH-1.3.0-07.2015

3. A student used his place value chart to show a number. After the teacher instructed him to multiply his number by 10, the chart showed 3,200.4. Draw a picture of what the place value chart looked like at first.

> 3 hundreds times 10 is 3 thousands. The original number must have had a 3 in the hundreds place.

thousands	hundreds	tens	ones	●	tenths	hundredths	thousandths
	3	2	0	.	0	4	

> I used the place value chart to help me visualize what the original number was. When multiplying by 10, each digit must have shifted 1 place to the left, so I shifted each digit 1 place back to the right to show the original number.

4. A microscope has a setting that magnifies an object so that it appears 100 times as large when viewed through the eyepiece. If a small bug is 0.183 cm long, how long will the insect appear in centimeters through the microscope? Explain how you know.

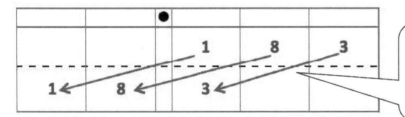

> When multiplying by 100, each digit shifts 2 places to the *left* on the place value chart.

The bug will appear to be 18.3 cm long through the microscope.

Since the microscope magnifies objects 100 times, the bug will appear to be 100 times larger. I used a place value chart to show what happens to the value of each digit when it is multiplied by 100. Each digit shifts 2 places to the left.

EUREKA
MATH

©2015 Great Minds. eureka-math.org
G5-M1-HWH-1.3.0-07.2015

G5-M1-Lesson 2

1. Solve.

   a. $4{,}258 \times 10 =$ __42,580__

   > I visualized a place value chart. 8 ones times 10 is 8 tens. When multiplying by 10, each digit shifts 1 place to the *left*.

   c. $3.9 \times 100 =$ __390__

   > The factor 100, has 2 zeros, so I can visualize each digit shifting 2 places to the *left*.

   b. $4{,}258 \div 10 =$ __425.8__

   > When dividing by 10, each digit shifts 1 place to the *right*.

   d. $3.9 \div 100 =$ __0.039__

   > The divisor, 100, has 2 zeros, so each digit shifts 2 places to the *right*.

2. Solve.

   > 7×1 hundred $= 7$ hundreds $= 700$

   a. $9{,}647 \times 100 =$ __964,700__

   > $7 \div 1$ thousand $= 7$ thousandths $= 0.007$

   b. $9{,}647 \div 1{,}000 =$ __9.647__

   c. Explain how you decided on the number of zeros in the product for part (a).

   I visualized a place value chart. Multiplying by 100 shifts each digit in the factor 9,647 two places to the left, so there were 2 additional zeros in the product.

   d. Explain how you decided where to place the decimal in the quotient for part (b).

   The divisor, 1,000, has 3 zeros, so each digit in 9,647 shifts 3 places to the right. When the digit 9 shifts 3 places to the right, it moves to the ones places, so I knew the decimal point needed to go between the ones place and the tenths place. I put the decimal between the 9 and the 6.

 EUREKA MATH   Lesson 2: Reason abstractly using place value understanding to relate adjacent base ten units from millions to thousandths.   3

©2015 Great Minds. eureka-math.org
G5-M1-HWH-1.3.0-07.2015

3. Jasmine says that 7 hundredths multiplied by 1,000 equals 7 thousands. Is she correct? Use a place value chart to explain your answer.

   Jasmine is not correct. 7 ones × 1,000 would be 7 thousands.

   But 0.07 × 1,000 = 70. Look at my place value chart.

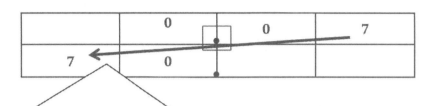

   The factor 1,000 has 3 zeros, so the digit 7 shifts 3 places to the left on the place value chart.

4. Nino's class earned $750 selling candy bars for a fundraiser. $\frac{1}{10}$ of all the money collected was from sales made by Nino. How much money did Nino raise?

   The whole tape represents all of the money earned by Nino's class.

   Nino collected $\frac{1}{10}$ of all the money, so I partition the tape diagram into 10 equal

   $750

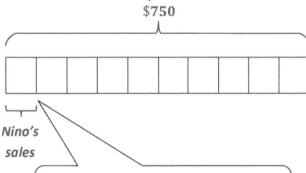

   Nino's sales

   The value of this 1 unit will tell me how much money Nino earned for his class.

   10 units = $750

   1 unit = $750 ÷ 10

   1 unit = $75

   Nino raised $75.

Lesson 2: Reason abstractly using place value understanding to relate adjacent base ten units from millions to thousandths.

EUREKA MATH

G5-M1-Lesson 3

1. Write the following in exponential form.

    a. $10 \times 10 \times 10 = \underline{10^3}$

    > 10 is a factor 3 times, so the exponent is 3. I can read this as, "ten to the third power."

    c. $100,000 = \underline{10^5}$

    b. $1,000 \times 10 = \underline{10^4}$

    d. $100 = \underline{10^2}$

    > $1,000 = 10 \times 10 \times 10$, so this expression uses 10 as a factor 4 times. The exponent is 4.

    > I recognize a pattern. 100 has 2 zeros. Therefore, the exponent is 2. One hundred equals 10 to the 2nd power.

2. Write the following in standard form.

    a. $6 \times 10^3 = \underline{6,000}$

    > 10^3 is equal to 1,000. 6 times 1 thousand is 6 thousand.

    c. $643 \div 10^3 = \underline{0.643}$

    b. $60.43 \times 10^4 = \underline{604,300}$

    d. $6.4 \div 10^2 = \underline{0.064}$

    > The exponent 4 tells me how many places each digit will shift to the left.

    > The exponent 2 tells me how many places each digit will shift to the right.

3. Complete the patterns.

    a. 0.06   0.6 $\underline{6}$ 60 $\underline{600}$ $\underline{6,000}$

    > 6 tenths is larger than 6 hundredths. Each number in the pattern is 10 times larger than the previous number.

    b. $\underline{92,100}$ 9,210 $\underline{921}$ 92.1   9.21 $\underline{0.921}$

    > The numbers are getting smaller in this pattern.

    > The digits have each shifted 1 place to the right. The pattern in this sequence is "divide by 10^1."

EUREKA MATH   Lesson 3:   Use exponents to name place value units and explain patterns in the   5
                                  placement of the decimal point.

©2015 Great Minds. eureka-math.org
G5-M1-HWH-1.3.0-07.2015

G5-M1-Lesson 4

1. Convert and write an equation with an exponent.

> In the first 2 problems, I am converting a *larger* unit to a *smaller* unit. Therefore, I need to multiply to find the equivalent length.

| 1 meter is equal to 100 centimeters. |

a. 4 meters to centimeters   ___4___ m = __400__ cm $4 \times 10^2 = 400$

| 1 meter is equal to 1,000 millimeters. |

b. 2.8 meters to millimeters   __2.8__ m = _2,800_ mm $2.8 \times 10^3 = 2,800$

2. Convert using an equation with an exponent.

> In these 2 problems, I am converting a *smaller* unit to a *larger* unit. Therefore, I need to divide to find the equivalent length.

| There are 100 centimeters in 1 meter. |

a. 87 centimeters to meters   __87__ cm = _0.87_ m $87 \div 10^2 = 0.87$

| There are 1,000 millimeters in 1 meter. |

b. 9 millimeters to meters   __9__ mm = _0.009_ m $9 \div 10^3 = 0.009$

3. The height of a cellphone is 13 cm. Express this measurement in meters. Explain your thinking. Include an equation with an exponent in your explanation.

$$13 \text{ cm} = 0.13 \text{ m}$$

> In order to rename smaller units as larger units, I'll need to divide.

Since 1 meter is equal to 100 centimeters, I divided the number of centimeters by 100.

$$13 \div 10^2 = 0.13$$

> I need to include an equation with an exponent, so I'll express 100 as 10^2.

Lesson 4:   Use exponents to denote powers of 10 with application to metric
                 conversions.

©2015 Great Minds. eureka-math.org
G5-M1-HWH-1.3.0-07.2015

G5-M1-Lesson 5

1. Express as decimal numerals.

   a. Eight and three hundred fifty-two thousandths

      8.352

   b. $\frac{6}{100}$

      0.06

   c. $5\frac{132}{1000}$

      5.132

   > The word *and* separates the whole numbers from the decimal numbers.

   > I can rewrite this fraction as a decimal. There are zero ones and zero tenths in the fraction 6 *hundredths*.

2. Express in words.

   a. 0.034

      Thirty-four thousandths

   b. 73.29

      Seventy-three and twenty-nine hundredths

   > The word *and* separates the whole numbers from the decimal numbers.

3. Write the number in expanded form using decimals and fractions.

   303.084

   $3 \times 100 + 3 \times 1 + 8 \times 0.01 + 4 \times 0.001$

   $3 \times 100 + 3 \times 1 + 8 \times \frac{1}{100} + 4 \times \frac{1}{1000}$

   > This expanded form uses decimals. 8 hundredths is the same as 8 units of 1 hundredth or (8×0.01).

   > This expanded form uses fractions. $\frac{1}{1000} = 0.001$. Both are read as

EUREKA MATH

Lesson 5: Name decimal fractions in expanded, unit, and word forms by applying place value reasoning.

©2015 Great Minds. eureka-math.org
G5-M1-HWH-1.3.0-07.2015

7

4. Write a decimal for each of the following.

   a. $4 \times 100 + 5 \times 1 + 2 \times \frac{1}{10} + 8 \times \frac{1}{1000}$

   405.208

   > There are 0 tens and 0 hundredths in expanded form, so I wrote 0 tens and 0 hundredths in standard form too.

   b. $9 \times 1 + 9 \times 0.1 + 3 \times 0.01 + 6 \times 0.001$

   9.936

   > 3×0.01 is 3 units of 1 hundredth, which I can write as a 3 in the hundredths place.

Lesson 5:   Name decimal fractions in expanded, unit, and word forms by applying place value reasoning.

©2015 Great Minds. eureka-math.org
G5-M1-HWH-1.3.0-07.2015

G5-M1-Lesson 6

1. Show the numbers on the place value chart using digits. Use >, <, or = to compare.

   43.554 $\underline{>}$ 43.545

	4	3	5	5	4
	4	3	5	4	5

   I put each digit of both numbers in the place value chart. Now I can easily compare the values.

   5 hundredths is greater than 4 hundredths. Therefore, 43.554 > 43.545.

2. Use the >, <, or = to compare the following.

   a. 7.4 $\underline{=}$ 74 tenths

   10 tenths = 1 one   20 tenths = 2 ones   70 tenths = 7 ones

   Therefore, 74 tenths = 7 ones and 4 tenths.

   b. 2.7 $\underline{>}$ Twenty-seven hundredths

   1 one = 10 tenths   2 ones = 20 tenths   2.7 = 27 tenths

   Tenths are a larger unit that hundredths, therefore 27 tenths is *greater* than 27 hundredths.

   c. 3.12 $\underline{<}$ 312 tenths

   I can think of both numbers in unit form: 312 hundredths < 312 tenths. Hundredths are a smaller unit than tenths.

   I can also think of both numbers in decimal notation: 3.12 < 31.2.

   d. 1.17 $\underline{>}$ 1.165

   Both of these numbers have 1 one and 1 tenth. But 7 hundredths is *greater* than 6 hundredths. I know that 1.17 is *greater* than 1.165.

   I need to be careful! Although 1.165 has more digits than 1.17, it doesn't always mean it has a greater value.

   I also know that 1.17 = 1.170. When both numbers have the same number of digits, I can clearly see that 1.170 > 1.165.

Lesson 6:   Compare decimal fractions to the thousandths using like units and express comparisons with >, <, =.

©2015 Great Minds. eureka-math.org
G5-M1-HWH-1.3.0-07.2015

9

3. Arrange the numbers in *increasing* order.

    8.719   8.79   8.7   8.179

    8.179,   8.7,   8.719,   8.79
    _____

> Increasing order means I need to list the numbers from *least* to *greatest*.

8	7	1	9
8	7	9	
8	7		
8	1	7	9

> To make comparing easier, I'm going to use a place value chart.

> The 9 hundredths is greater than all of the other digits in the hundredths place. 8.79 is the largest number.

> All of the numbers have 8 ones. 1 tenth is less than 7 tenths, so 8.179 is the smallest number.

> Decreasing order means I need to list the numbers from *greatest* to *least*.

4. Arrange the numbers in *decreasing* order.

    56.128   56.12   56.19   56.182

    56.19,   56.182,   56.128,   56.12
    _____

> This time I'll just visualize the place value chart in my head.

> I'll begin by comparing the largest units, tens, first. All of the numbers have 5 tens, 6 ones, and 1 tenth. I'll look to the hundredths place next to compare.

> Even though this number has only 4 digits, it's actually the largest number. The 9 in the hundredths place is the largest of all the digits in the hundredths places.

> When I compare 56.12 and 56.128 to the other numbers, I see that they both have the fewest number of hundredths. However, I know that 56.128 is larger because it has 8 thousandths more than 56.12.

Lesson 6:   Compare decimal fractions to the thousandths using like units and
            express comparisons with >, <, =.

EUREKA MATH

©2015 Great Minds. eureka-math.org
G5-M1-HWH-1.3.0-07.2015

G5-M1-Lesson 7

Round to the given place value. Label the number lines to show your work. Circle the rounded number. Use a place value chart to show your decompositions for each.

1. 3.27

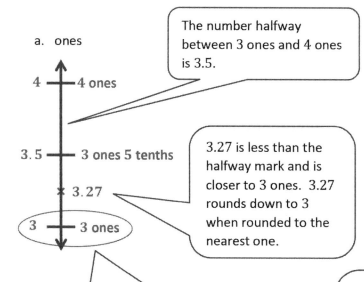

a. ones

The number halfway between 3 ones and 4 ones is 3.5.

4 —— 4 ones

3.5 —— 3 ones 5 tenths

✗ 3.27

⟨3 —— 3 ones⟩

3.27 is less than the halfway mark and is closer to 3 ones. 3.27 rounds down to 3 when rounded to the nearest one.

I know that 3.27 lies somewhere between 3 ones and 4 ones on the number line. When rounding to the nearest one, I need to identify if it's closer to 3 ones or 4 ones.

b. tenths

⟨3.3 —— 33 tenths⟩

✗ 3.27

3.25 —— 32 tenths 5 hundredths

3.2 —— 32 tenths

3.27 is more than the halfway mark and is closer to 33 tenths. 3.27 rounds up to 3.3 when rounded to the nearest tenth.

The number halfway between 32 tenths and 33 tenths is 3.25.

In order to round 3.27 to the nearest tenth, I need to know how many tenths are in 3.27. The chart below tells me that there are 32 tenths in 3.27.

ones	tenths	hundredths
3	2	7
	32	7
		327

I can think of 3.27 in several ways. I can say it is 3 ones +2 tenths +7 hundredths. I can also think of it as 32 tenths +7 hundredths or 327 hundredths.

Lesson 7:   Round a given decimal to any place using place value understanding and   11
             the vertical number line.

©2015 Great Minds. eureka-math.org
G5-M1-HWH-1.3.0-07.2015

2. Rosie's pedometer said she walked 1.46 miles. She rounded her distance to 1 mile, and her brother, Isaac, rounded her distance to 1.5 miles. They are both right. Why?

Rosie rounded the distance to the nearest mile, and Isaac rounded the distance to the nearest tenth of a mile.

1.46 rounded to the nearest one is 1.   *1.46 rounded to the nearest tenth*

                                                               is 15 tenths or 1.5.

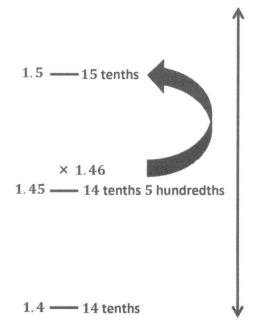

2 ── 2 ones

1.5 ── 1 one 5 tenths
1.46 ✗
                                                               1.5 ── 15 tenths

                                                               × 1.46
                                                               1.45 ── 14 tenths 5 hundredths

1 ── 1 one   1.4 ── 14 tenths

12   Lesson 7:   Round a given decimal to any place using place value understanding and
                            the vertical number line.

©2015 Great Minds. eureka-math.org
G5-M1-HWH-1.3.0-07.2015

EUREKA
MATH

G5-M1-Lesson 8

1. Round the quantity to the given place value. Draw number lines to explain your thinking. Circle the rounded value on the number line.

Round 23.245 to the nearest tenth and hundredth.

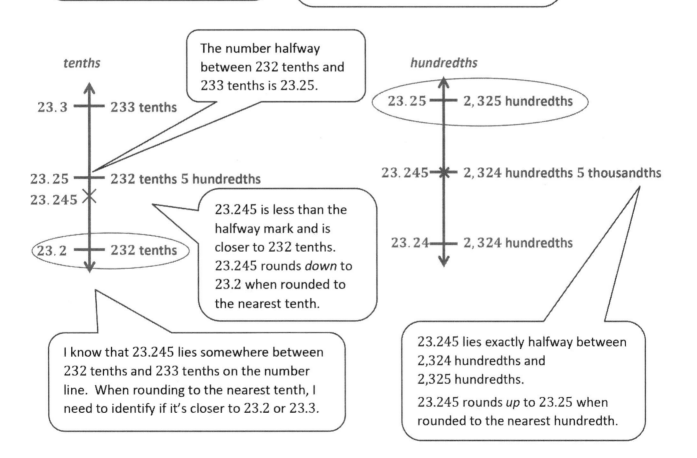

2 tens = 200 tenths

3 ones = 30 tenths

There are 232 tenths
4 hundredths 5 thousandths in
the number 23.245.

2 tens = 2,000 hundredths

3 ones = 300 hundredths

2 tenths = 20 hundredths

There are 2,324 hundredths
5 thousandths in the number 23.245.

tenths

The number halfway
between 232 tenths and
233 tenths is 23.25.

hundredths

23.3 —— 233 tenths

23.25 —— 2,325 hundredths

23.25 —— 232 tenths 5 hundredths

23.245 ✗

23.245 is less than the
halfway mark and is
closer to 232 tenths.
23.245 rounds *down* to
23.2 when rounded to
the nearest tenth.

23.245 —✗— 2,324 hundredths 5 thousandths

23.24 —— 2,324 hundredths

23.2 —— 232 tenths

I know that 23.245 lies somewhere between
232 tenths and 233 tenths on the number
line. When rounding to the nearest tenth, I
need to identify if it's closer to 23.2 or 23.3.

23.245 lies exactly halfway between
2,324 hundredths and
2,325 hundredths.

23.245 rounds *up* to 23.25 when
rounded to the nearest hundredth.

EUREKA
MATH™   Lesson 8:   Round a given decimal to any place using place value understanding and
                                  the vertical number line.   13

2. A decimal number has two digits to the right of its decimal point. If we round it to the nearest tenth, the result is 28.7. What is the maximum possible value of this decimal? Use words and the number line to explain your reasoning.

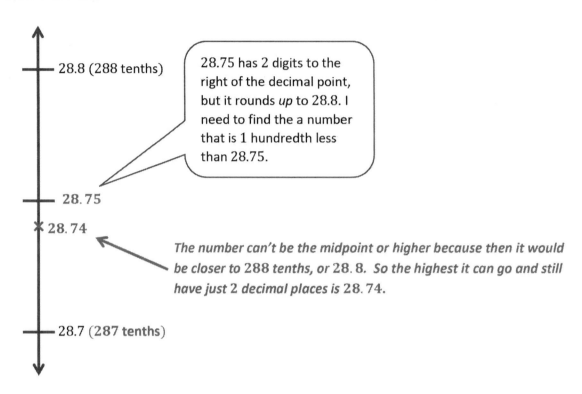

28.8 (288 tenths)

28.75 has 2 digits to the right of the decimal point, but it rounds *up* to 28.8. I need to find the a number that is 1 hundredth less than 28.75.

28.75

✗ 28.74

The number can't be the midpoint or higher because then it would be closer to 288 tenths, or 28.8. So the highest it can go and still have just 2 decimal places is 28.74.

28.7 (287 tenths)

EUREKA
MATH

G5-M1-Lesson 9

Note: Adding decimals is just like adding whole numbers—combine like units. Study the examples below:

  2 apples + 3 apples = 5 apples

  2 ones + 3 ones = 5 ones

  2 tens + 3 tens = 5 tens = 50

  2 hundredths + 3 hundredths = 5 hundredths = 0.05

1. Solve.

I'll combine the like units, tenths, to get 5 tenths.

  a.   2 tenths + 3 tenths = ____5____ tenths

The standard form is $0.2 + 0.3 = 0.5$.

I'll combine the like units, hundredths, and get 31 hundredths.

  b.   26 hundredths + 5 hundredths = __31__ hundredths = _3_ tenths _1_ hundredths

The standard form is $0.26 + 0.05 = 0.31$.

10 hundredths = 1 tenth
20 hundredths = 2 tenths
30 hundredths = 3 tenths

I'll combine the like units and get 5 ones 6 tenths, which is the same as 56 tenths.

  c.   5 ones 2 tenths + 4 tenths = ____56____ tenths

1 one = 10 tenths
5 ones = 50 tenths

The standard form is $5.2 + 0.4 = 5.6$.

EUREKA MATH   Lesson 9:   Add decimals using place value strategies, and relate those strategies to a written method.   15

©2015 Great Minds. eureka-math.org
G5-M1-HWH-1.3.0-07.2015

2. Solve using the standard algorithm.

a. $0.3 + 0.91 = \underline{1.21}$

> 3 tenths + 9 tenths is 12 tenths. I'll record 12 tenths as 1 one and 2 tenths.

> When setting up the algorithm, I need to be sure to add like units. Therefore I'll line up the tens with the tens, the ones with the ones et cetera.

b. $75.604 + 12.087 = \underline{87.691}$

$$
\begin{array}{r}
7\,5.6\,0\,4 \\
+\ 1\,2.0\,8\,7 \\
\hline
{\scriptstyle 1} \\
8\,7.6\,9\,1 \\
\end{array}
$$

> 4 thousandths + 7 thousandths is 11 thousandths. I'll record 11 thousandths as 1 hundredth 1 thousandth.

3. Anthony spends $6.49 on a book. He also buys a pencil for $2.87 and an eraser for $1.15. How much money does he spend altogether?

$\$6.49 + \$2.87 + \$1.15 = \$10.51$

> I'll add all three items together to find the total price.

$$
\begin{array}{r}
6.4\,9 \\
2.8\,7 \\
+1.1\,5 \\
\hline
{\scriptstyle 1\ 2} \\
1\,0.5\,1 \\
\end{array}
$$

> 9 hundredths + 7 hundredths + 5 hundredths is 21 hundredths. I'll record 21 hundredths as 2 tenths 1 hundredth.

> 4 tenths + 8 tenths + 1 tenth + 2 tenths is 15 tenths. I'll record 15 tenths as 1 one and 5 tenths.

Anthony spends $10.51.

Lesson 9:   Add decimals using place value strategies, and relate those strategies to a written method.

EUREKA MATH

G5-M1-Lesson 10

Note: Subtracting decimals is just like subtracting whole numbers—subtract like units. Study the examples below.

5 apples −1 apple = 4 apples
5 ones −1 one = 4 ones
5 tens −1 ten = 4 tens
5 hundredths −1 hundredth = 4 hundredths

1. Subtract.

> I'll subtract the like units, tenths, to get 3 tenths.

   a.   7 tenths −4 tenths = ____3____ tenths

> The standard form is $0.7 − 0.4 = 0.3$.

> I'll subtract 3 hundredths from 8 hundredths, and get 5 hundredths.

> I'll look at the units carefully.
> A *hundred* is different than a *hundredth*.

   b.   4 hundreds 8 hundredths −3 hundredths = ___4___ hundreds ___5___ hundredths

> The standard form is $400.08 − 0.03 = 400.05$.

> 1.7 is the same as 1.70.

2. Solve $1.7 − 0.09$ using the standard algorithm.

> There are 0 hundredths, so I can't subtract 9 hundredths. I'll rename 7 tenths as 6 tenths 10 hundredths.

> When setting up the algorithm, I need to be sure to subtract like units. Therefore, I'll line up the ones with the ones, the tenths with the tenths. etc.

```
      6  10
 1.  7̸  0̸
-0.  0  9
_____
 1.  6  1
```

> 10 hundredths minus 9 hundredths is equal to 1 hundredth.

EUREKA
MATH™

Lesson 10:   Submit decimals using place value strategies, and relate those strategies
              to a written method.

17

©2015 Great Minds. eureka-math.org
G5-M1-HWH-1.3.0-07.2015

6 ones 3 tenths = 6.3 = 6.30
58 hundredths = 0.58

3. Solve 6 ones 3 tenths −58 hundredths.

There are 0 hundredths, so I can't subtract
8 hundredths. I'll rename 3 tenths as 2
tenths 10 hundredths.

I'll rename 6 ones as 5 ones
10 tenths. 10 tenths, plus the
2 tenths already there, makes
12 tenths.

```
    5   12  10
    6.  3   0
  − 0.  5   8
  ─────────────
    5.  7   2
```

10 hundredths minus 8 hundredths is
equal to 2 hundredths.

Students can solve using a variety of methods. This problem may not require
the standard algorithm as some students can compute mentally.

4. A pen costs $2.57. It costs $0.49 more than a ruler. Kayla bought two pens and one ruler. She paid with
a ten-dollar bill. How much change does Kayla get? Use a tape diagram to show your thinking.

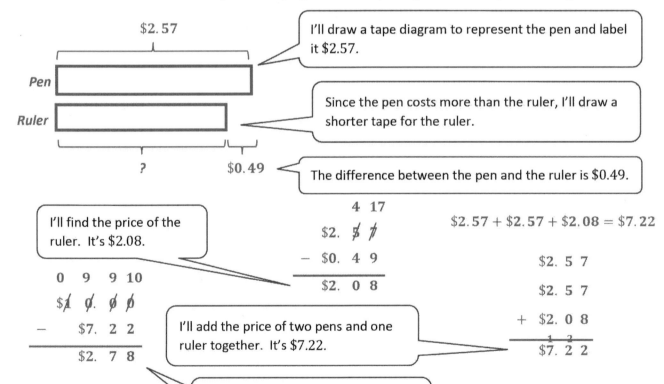

$2.57

I'll draw a tape diagram to represent the pen and label
it $2.57.

Pen

Since the pen costs more than the ruler, I'll draw a
shorter tape for the ruler.

Ruler

? $0.49

The difference between the pen and the ruler is $0.49.

I'll find the price of the
ruler. It's $2.08.

```
      4   17
  $2.  5   7
− $0.  4   9
─────────────
  $2.  0   8
```

$2.57 + $2.57 + $2.08 = $7.22

```
    0   9   9  10
  $ 1  0.  0   0
−      $7. 2   2
──────────────────
       $2. 7   8
```

I'll add the price of two pens and one
ruler together. It's $7.22.

```
    $2.  5   7
    $2.  5   7
  + $2.  0   8
  ─────────────
    $7.  2   2
```

Kayla's change is $2.78.

I'll subtract the total cost from $10.
Kayla's change will be $2.78.

Lesson 10:   Submit decimals using place value strategies, and relate those strategies
to a written method.

EUREKA
MATH

Note: Encourage your child to use a variety of strategies when solving. The standard algorithm may not always be necessary for some students. Ask them about different ways to solve the problem. Below you'll find some alternate solution strategies that could be applied.

$2.57 + $2.57 + $2.08 = $7.22

When finding the total cost of the 3 items, I can think of adding $2.50 + $2.50 + $2, which is equal to $7. Then I'll add the remaining 7¢ + 7¢ + 8¢, which is 22¢. The total then, is $7 + $0.22 = $7.22. I can do all of this mentally!

Then when finding the amount of change Kayla gets, I can use another strategy to solve.

Instead of finding the difference of $10 and $7.22 using the subtraction algorithm, I can count up from $7.22.

$$ \$7.22 \xrightarrow{+3¢} \$7.25 \xrightarrow{+75¢} \$8.00 \xrightarrow{+\$2} \$10.00 $$

3¢ more makes $7.25.

3 quarters, or 75 cents, more makes $8.

$2 more makes $10.

2 dollars, 3 quarters, and 3 pennies is $2.78. That's what Kayla gets back.

Kayla gets $2.78 back in change.

EUREKA MATH   Lesson 10:   Submit decimals using place value strategies, and relate those strategies   19
to a written method.

©2015 Great Minds. eureka-math.org
G5-M1-HWH-1.3.0-07.2015

G5-M1-Lesson 11

1. Solve by drawing disks on a place value chart. Write an equation, and express the product in standard form.

   a. 2 copies of 4 tenths

   $= 2 \times 0.4$

   $= 0.8$

   > 2 copies means 2 groups. So, I'll multiply 2 times 4 tenths. The answer is 8 tenths, or 0.8.

   > I'll draw a place value chart to help me solve, and this dot is the decimal point.

Ones	Tenths
	● ● ● ●
	● ● ● ●

   > Each dot represents 1 tenth, so I'll draw 2 groups of 4 tenths.

   b. 3 times as much as 6 hundredths

   $= 3 \times 0.06$

   $= 0.18$

   > I'll multiply 3 times 6 hundredths. The answer is 18 hundredths, or 0.18.

   > I'll draw 3 groups of 6 hundredths.

   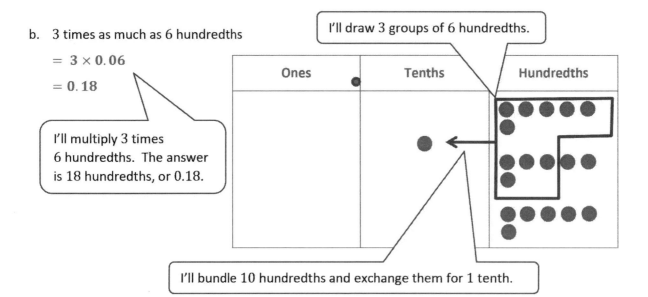

Ones	Tenths	Hundredths

   > I'll bundle 10 hundredths and exchange them for 1 tenth.

Lesson 11:   Multiply a decimal fraction by single- digit whole numbers, relate to a written method through application of the area model and place value understanding, and explain the reasoning used.

©2015 Great Minds. eureka-math.org
G5-M1-HWH-1.3.0-07.2015

EUREKA
MATH

2. Draw an area model, and find the sum of the partial products to evaluate each expression.

a. 2×3.17 ◄─── 3.17 is the same as 3 ones 1 tenth 7 hundredths.

The factor 3.17 represents the length of the area model.

The factor 2 represents the width of the area model.

	3 ones	+	1 tenth	+ 7 hundredths
2	2×3 ones		2×1 tenth	2×7 hundredths

        6   +   0.2   +   0.14   =   6.34

I'll multiply 2 times each place value unit.

2×3 ones $= 6$ ones $= 6$

2×1 tenth $= 2$ tenths $= 0.2$

2×7 hundredths $= 14$ hundredths $= 0.14$

The product of 2 and 3.17 is 6.34.

b. 4 times as much as 30.162 ◄─── There are 0 ones in 30.162, so my area model does not include the ones.

	3 tens	+	1 tenth	+ 6 hundredths	+ 2 thousandths
4	4×3 tens		4×1 tenth	4×6 hundredths	4×2 thousandths

      120   +   0.4   +   0.24   +   0.008 =   120.648

I'll multiply 4 times each place value unit.

4×3 tens $= 12$ tens $= 120$

4×1 tenth $= 4$ tenths $= 0.4$

4×6 hundredths $= 24$ hundredths $= 0.24$

4×2 thousandths $= 8$ thousandths $= 0.008$

The product of 4 and 30.162 is 120.648.

EUREKA MATH   Lesson 11:   Multiply a decimal fraction by single- digit whole numbers, relate to a
written method through application of the area model and place value
understanding, and explain the reasoning used.   21

©2015 Great Minds. eureka-math.org
G5-M1-HWH-1.3.0-07.2015

G5-M1-Lesson 12

1. Choose the reasonable product for each expression. Explain your thinking in the spaces below using words, pictures, or numbers.

   a. 3.1×3 930   93   9.3   0.93

   > 3.1 is just a little more than 3. A reasonable product would be just a little more than 9.

   $3 \times 3 = 9$. I looked for a product that was close to 9.

   b. 8×7.036 5.6288   56.288   562.88   5,628.8

   > This product is not reasonable. How could 8×7.036 be less than both factors?

   > These 2 products are much too large.

   $8 \times 7 = 56$. I looked for a product that was close to 56.

2. Lenox weighs 9.2 kg. Her older brother is 3 times as heavy as Lenox. How much does her older brother weigh in kilograms?

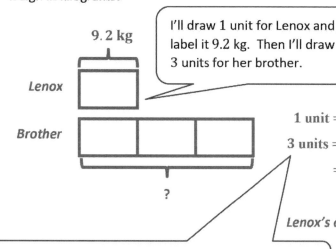

   I'll draw 1 unit for Lenox and label it 9.2 kg. Then I'll draw 3 units for her brother.

   I can visualize an area model to solve 3×9.2.

   3×9 ones $= 27$ ones $= 27$

   3×2 tenths $= 6$ tenths $= 0.6$

   $27 + 0.6 = 27.6$

   1 unit $= 9.2$ kg

   3 units $= 3 \times 9.2$ kg

   $= 27.6$ kg

   Lenox's older brother weighs 27.6 kilograms.

   To find her brother's weight, I'll multiply Lenox's weight by 3. The answer is 27.6 kilograms.

G5-M1-Lesson 13

Note: The use of unit language (e.g., 21 hundredths rather than 0.21) allows students to use knowledge of basic facts to compute easily with decimals.

1. Complete the sentence with the correct number of units, and then complete the equation.

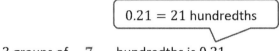

$$0.21 = 21 \text{ hundredths}$$

3 groups of __7__ hundredths is 0.21.

$0.21 \div 3 =$ __0.07__

I know the basic fact $3 \times 7 = 21$. This is similar.

3×7 hundredths $= 21$ hundredths

Since $21 \div 3 = 7$, then

21 hundredths $\div 3 = 7$ hundredths

2. Complete the number sentence. Express the quotient in units and then in standard form.

Since the divisor is 4, I'll decompose 8.16 into 8 ones and 16 hundredths. Both 8 and 16 are multiples of 4.

a. $8.16 \div 4 =$ ___8___ ones $\div 4 +$ ___16___ hundredths $\div 4$

$= $ ___2___ ones $+$ ___4___ hundredths

8 ones $\div 4 = 2$ ones $= 2$

$= $ ___2.04___

16 hundredths $\div 4 = 4$ hundredths $= 0.04$

$2 + 0.04 = 2.04$

Since the divisor is 6, I'll decompose 1.242 into 12 tenths and 42 thousandths. Both 12 and 42 are multiples of 6.

b. $1.242 \div 6 =$ ___$(12 \text{ tenths} \div 6) + (42 \text{ thousandths} \div 6)$___

$= $ ___$2 \text{ tenths} + 7 \text{ thousandths}$___

12 tenths $\div 6 = 2$ tenths $= 0.2$

$= $ ___0.207___

42 thousandths $\div 6 = 7$ thousandths $= 0.007$

EUREKA MATH™

Lesson 13: Divide decimals by single-digit whole numbers involving easily identifiable multiples using place value understanding and relate to a written method.

23

©2015 Great Minds. eureka-math.org
G5-M1-HWH-1.3.0-07.2015

3. Find the quotients. Then, use words, numbers, or pictures to describe any relationships you notice between the pair of problems and their quotients.

   a. $35 \div 5 =$ ___7___

   b. $3.5 \div 5 =$ ___0.7___

   I know this basic fact!

   I can use that basic fact to help me solve this one.

   35 tenths $\div$ 5 = 7 tenths = 0.7

   Both problems are dividing by 5, but the quotient for part (a) is 10 times larger than the quotient for (b). That makes sense because the number we started with in part (a) is also 10 times larger than the number we started with in part (b).

4. Is the quotient below reasonable? Explain your answer.

   a. $0.56 \div 7 = 8$

   56 hundredths $\div$ 7 = 8 hundredths

   0.56 = 56 hundredths

   No, the quotient is not reasonable.

   $56 \div 7 = 8$, *so 56 hundredths* $\div$ *7 must be 8 hundredths.*

5. A toy airplane weighs 3.69 kg. It weighs 3 times as much as a toy car. What is the weight of the toy car?

   I draw 1 tape diagram to show the weight of the airplane.

   $3.69\ kg$

   airplane

   car

   ?

   The car is equal to the weight of 1 unit.

   The airplane weighs 3 times as much as the car, so I partition the tape diagram, into 3 equal units.

   I can use unit language and basic facts to solve.

   3 ones $\div$ 3 = 1 one

   6 tenths $\div$ 3 = 2 tenths = 0.2

   9 hundredths $\div$ 3 = 3 hundredths = 0.03

   3 units = 3.69

   1 unit = 3.69 $\div$ 3

   1 unit = 1.23

   The toy car weighs .23 kg.

Lesson 13:   Divide decimals by single-digit whole numbers involving easily identifiable multiples using place value understanding and relate to a written method.

©2015 Great Minds. eureka-math.org
G5-M1-HWH-1.3.0-07.2015

EUREKA
MATH

G5-M1-Lesson 14

1. Draw place value disks on the place value chart to solve. Show each step using the standard algorithm.

$4.272 \div 3 = \underline{1.424}$

> 4.272 is divided into 3 equal groups. There is 1.424 in each group.

Ones	Tenths	Hundredths	Thousandths

```
    1.  4  2  4
  3 | 4.  2  7  2
    - 3
    ---------
       1  2
     - 1  2
    ---------
          0  7
        -    6
    ---------
             1  2
           - 1  2
    ---------
                0
```

> When I share 4 ones equally with 3 groups, there is 1 one in each group and 1 one remaining.

> In order to continue sharing, or dividing, I'll exchange the 1 remaining hundredth for 10 thousandths.

> In each group, there is 1 one 4 tenths 2 hundredths 4 thousandths, or 1.424.

2. Solve 15.704 ÷ 4 using the standard algorithm.

> 15.704 is divided into 4 equal groups. There is 3.926 in each group.

```
      3.  9  2  6
  4 | 1  5.  7  0  4
    - 1  2
    ---------
         3  7
       - 3  6
    ---------
            1  0
          -    8
    ---------
               2  4
             - 2  4
    ---------
                  0
```

> When completing the division, I need to be sure to line up the place value units carefully—the tens with the tens, the ones with the ones, etc.

> As I work, I'm visualizing the place value chart and thinking out loud. "We had 15 ones and shared 12 of them. 3 ones remain. I can change those 3 ones for 30 tenths, which combined with the 7 tenths in the whole, makes 37 tenths. Now I need to share 37 tenths equally with 4 groups. Each group gets 9 tenths."

3. Mr. Huynh paid $85.44 for 6 pounds of cashews. What's the cost of 1 pound of cashews?

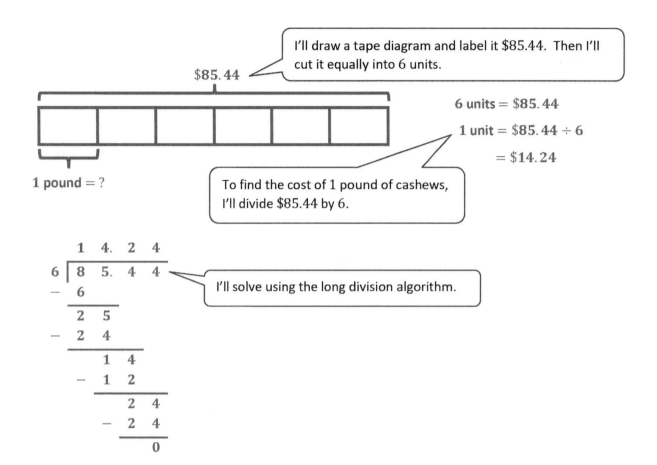

I'll draw a tape diagram and label it $85.44. Then I'll cut it equally into 6 units.

$85.44

6 units = $85.44

1 unit = $85.44 ÷ 6

= $14.24

1 pound = ?

To find the cost of 1 pound of cashews, I'll divide $85.44 by 6.

```
        1   4.  2   4
   6  | 8   5.  4   4
     -  6
        2   5
     -  2   4
            1   4
         -  1   2
                2   4
             -  2   4
                    0
```

I'll solve using the long division algorithm.

The cost of 1 pound of cashews is $14.24.

Lesson 14:   Divide decimals using place value understanding, including remainders in
              the smallest unit.

©2015 Great Minds. eureka-math.org
G5-M1-HWH-1.3.0-07.2015

EUREKA
MATH

G5-M1-Lesson 15

1. Draw place value disks on the place value chart to solve. Show each step in the standard algorithm.

$5.3 \div 4 = $ __1.325__

> 5.3 is divided into 4 equal groups
> There is 1.325 in each group.

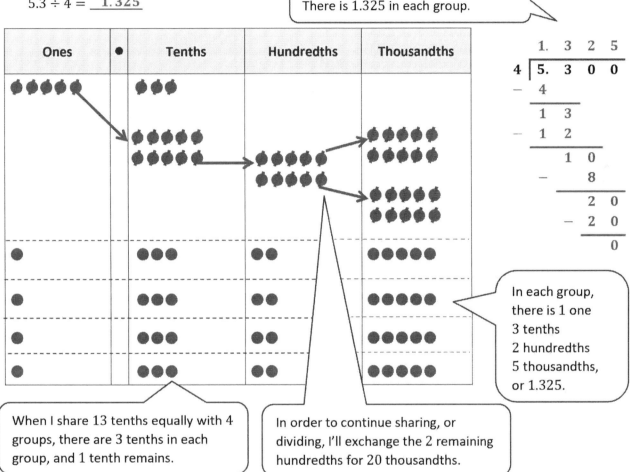

> In each group,
> there is 1 one
> 3 tenths
> 2 hundredths
> 5 thousandths,
> or 1.325.

> When I share 13 tenths equally with 4 groups, there are 3 tenths in each group, and 1 tenth remains.

> In order to continue sharing, or dividing, I'll exchange the 2 remaining hundredths for 20 thousandths.

2. Solve using the standard algorithm.

$9 \div 5 = $ __1.8__

> 9 is divided into 5 equal groups. There is 1.8 in each group.

> In order to continue dividing, I'll rename the 4 remaining ones as 40 tenths.
> 40 tenths ÷ 5 = 8 tenths

Lesson 15:   Divide decimals using place value understanding, including remainders ir the smallest unit.

©2015 Great Minds. eureka-math.org
G5-M1-HWH-1.3.0-07.2015

3. Four bakers shared 5.4 kilograms of sugar equally. How much sugar did they each receive?

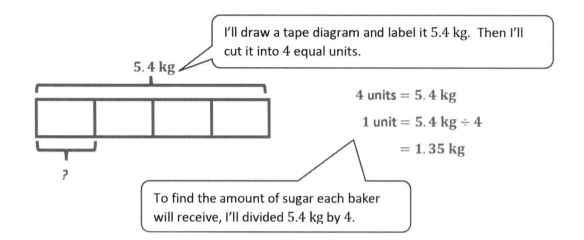

I'll draw a tape diagram and label it 5.4 kg. Then I'll cut it into 4 equal units.

5. 4 kg

4 units = 5. 4 kg

1 unit = 5. 4 kg ÷ 4

= 1. 35 kg

?

To find the amount of sugar each baker will receive, I'll divided 5.4 kg by 4.

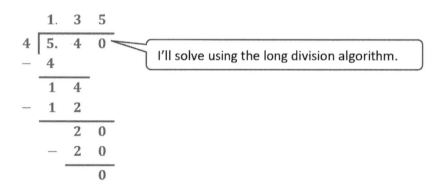

I'll solve using the long division algorithm.

Each baker received 1. 35 *kilograms of sugar.*

Lesson 15:   Divide decimals using place value understanding, including remainders ir
                            the smallest unit.

©2015 Great Minds. eureka-math.org
G5-M1-HWH-1.3.0-07.2015

**EUREKA
MATH**

G5-M1-Lesson 16

1. A comic book costs $6.47, and a cookbook costs $9.79.

    a. Zion buys 5 comic books and 3 cookbooks. What is the total cost for all of the books?

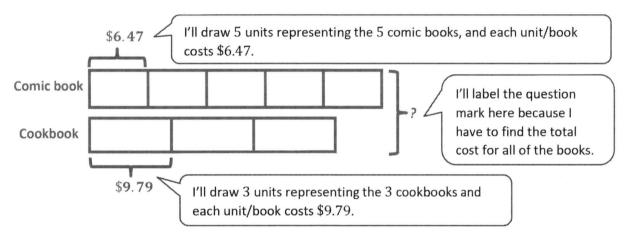

$6.47

I'll draw 5 units representing the 5 comic books, and each unit/book costs $6.47.

Comic book

I'll label the question mark here because I have to find the total cost for all of the books.

?

Cookbook

$9.79

I'll draw 3 units representing the 3 cookbooks and each unit/book costs $9.79.

Comic book:

1 unit = $6.47

5 units = 5 × $6.47 = $32.35

I'll find the total cost of the 5 comic books by multiplying 5 times $6.47.

	6 ones	+ 4 tenths	+ 7 hundredth
5	5 × 6 ones	5 × 4 tenths	5 × 7 hundredths
	30 ones	+ 20 tenth	+ 35 hundred = 32.35

Cookbook:

1 unit = $9.79

3 units = 3 × $9.79 = $29.37

I'll find the total cost of the 3 cookbooks by multiplying 3 times $9.79.

	9 ones	+ 7 tenths	+ 9 hundredth
3	3 × 9 ones	3 × 7 tenths	3 × 9 hundredths
	27 ones	+ 21 tent	+ 27 hundred = 29.37

The total cost of all the books is $61.72.

```
    3  2. 3  5
 +  2  9. 3  7
 ‾‾‾‾‾‾‾‾‾‾‾‾‾
    6  1. 7  2
```

I'll add the total cost of 5 comic books and the total cost of 3 cookbooks together to find the total cost of all 8 books.

b. Zion wants to pay for the all the books with a $100 bill. How much change will he get back?

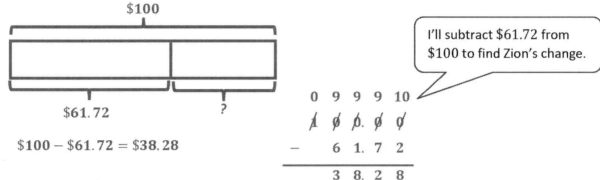

$100

$61.72   ?

I'll subtract $61.72 from $100 to find Zion's change.

$100 - $61.72 = $38.28

$$\begin{array}{r} {\overset{0}{\cancel{1}}}\;{\overset{9}{\cancel{0}}}\;{\overset{9}{\cancel{0}}}.{\overset{9}{\cancel{0}}}\;{\overset{10}{\cancel{0}}} \\ -\quad 6\;\;1.\;7\;\;2 \\ \hline 3\;\;8.\;2\;\;8 \end{array}$$

Zion will get $38.28 *back in change.*

2. Ms. Porter bought 40 meters of string. She used 8.5 meters to tie a package. Then she cuts the remainder into 6 equal pieces. Find the length of each piece. Give the answer in meters.

I'll draw a tape diagram to represent the string Ms. Porter bought and label the whole as 40 m.

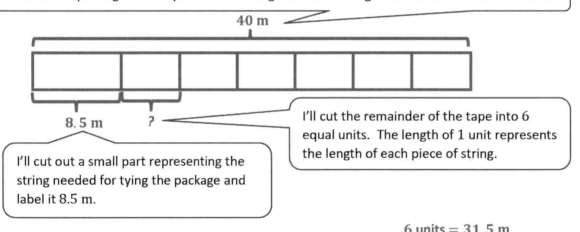

40 m

8.5 m   ?

I'll cut out a small part representing the string needed for tying the package and label it 8.5 m.

I'll cut the remainder of the tape into 6 equal units. The length of 1 unit represents the length of each piece of string.

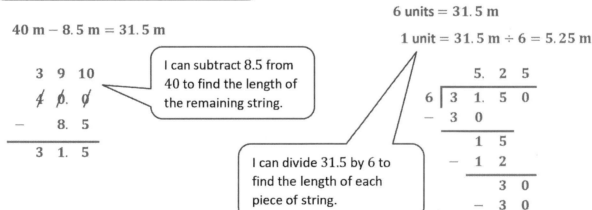

6 units = 31.5 m

1 unit = 31.5 m ÷ 6 = 5.25 m

40 m - 8.5 m = 31.5 m

$$\begin{array}{r} {\overset{3}{\cancel{4}}}\;{\overset{9}{\cancel{0}}}.{\overset{10}{\cancel{0}}} \\ -\quad\;\; 8.\;5 \\ \hline 3\;\;1.\;5 \end{array}$$

I can subtract 8.5 from 40 to find the length of the remaining string.

I can divide 31.5 by 6 to find the length of each piece of string.

$$\begin{array}{r} 5.\;2\;5 \\ 6\overline{\smash{)}3\;1.\;5\;0} \\ -3\;0 \\ \hline 1\;5 \\ -1\;2 \\ \hline 3\;0 \\ -\;3\;0 \\ \hline 0 \end{array}$$

Each piece of string is 5.25 *meters.*

Lesson 16:   Solve word problems using decimal operations.

EUREKA MATH™

Homework Helpers

Grade 5
Module 2

G5-M2-Lesson 1

1. Fill in the blanks using your knowledge of place value units and basic facts.

    a. 34×20

    Think: 34 ones $\times$ 2 tens = __68 tens__

    $34 \times 20 = $ __680__

    > 34 ones $\times$ 2 tens $= (34 \times 1) \times (2 \times 10)$.
    > First, I did the mental math: $34 \times 2 = 68$.
    > Then I thought about the units. *Ones times tens is tens.*
    > 68 tens is the same as 680 ones or 680.

    b. 420×20

    Think: 42 tens $\times$ 2 tens = __84 hundreds__

    $420 \times 20 = $ __8,400__

    > First, I'll multiply 42 times 2 in my head because that's a basic fact: 84.
    > Next, I have to think about the units. *Tens times tens is hundreds.*
    > Therefore, my answer is 84 hundreds or 8,400.

    > Another way to think about this is $42 \times 10 \times 2 \times 10$.
    > I can use the associative property to switch the order of the factors: $42 \times 2 \times 10 \times 10$.

    c. 400×500

    4 hundreds $\times$ 5 hundreds = __20 ten thousands__

    $400 \times 500 = $ __200,000__

    > I have to be careful because the basic fact, $4 \times 5 = 20$, ends in a zero.

    > Another way to think about this is $4 \times 100 \times 5 \times 100$
    > $= 4 \times 5 \times 100 \times 100$
    > $= 20 \times 100 \times 100$
    > $= 20 \times 10,000$
    > $= 200,000$

©2015 Great Minds. eureka-math.org
G5-M1-HWH-1.3.0-07.2015

2. Determine if these equations are true or false. Defend your answer using knowledge of place value and the commutative, associate, and/or distributive properties.

   a.   9 tens = 3 tens × 3 tens

   False. The basic fact is correct: $3 \times 3 = 9$.

   However, the units are not correct: 10×10 *is 100.*

   > Correct answers could be 9 tens = 3 tens × 3 ones, or 9 hundreds = 3 tens × 3 tens.

   b. $93 \times 7 \times 100 = 930 \times 7 \times 10$

   True. I can rewrite the problem. $93 \times 7 \times (10 \times 10) = (93 \times 10) \times 7 \times 10$

   > The associative property tells me that I can group the factors in any order without changing the product.

3. Find the products. Show your thinking.

   > I use the distributive property to decompose the factors.

60×5	60×50	$6,000 \times 5,000$
$= (6 \times 10) \times 5$	$= (6 \times 10) \times (5 \times 10)$	$= (6 \times 1,000) \times (5 \times 1,000)$
$= (6 \times 5) \times 10$	$= (6 \times 5) \times (10 \times 10)$	$= (6 \times 5) \times (1,000 \times 1,000)$
$= 30 \times 10$	$= 30 \times 100$	$= 30 \times 1,000,000$
$= 300$	$= 3,000$	$= 30,000,000$

   > Then, I use the associative property to regroup the factors.

   > I multiply the basic fact first. Then I think about the units.

   > I have to be careful because the basic fact, 6 × 5, has a zero in the product. I multiply the basic fact and then think about the units.
   >
   > 6 tens times 5 is 30 tens. 30 tens is the same as 300. I could get the wrong answer if I just counted zeros.

   > I can think of this in unit form: 6 thousands times 5 thousands. 6 × 5 = 30. The units are thousands times thousands. I can picture a place value chart in my head to solve a thousand times a thousand. A thousand times a thousand is a million. The answer is 30 million, or 30,000,000.

Lesson 1:   Multiply multi-digit whole numbers and multiples of 10 using place value patterns and the distributive and associative properties.

EUREKA MATH

G5-M2-Lesson 2

1. Round the factors to estimate the products.

> I round each factor to the largest unit.
> For example, 387 rounds to 400.

> The largest unit in 51 is tens. So, I round
> 51 to the nearest 10, which is 50.

    a. $387 \times 51 \approx \underline{\quad 400 \quad} \times \underline{\quad 50 \quad} = \underline{\quad 20,000 \quad}$

> Now that I have 2 rounded factors, I can use the
> distributive property to decompose the
> numbers. $400 \times 50 = (4 \times 100) \times (5 \times 10)$

> I can use the associative property to regroup the
> factors.
> $(4 \times 5) \times (100 \times 10) = 20 \times 1,000 = 20,000$

    b. $6,286 \times 26 \approx \underline{\quad 6,000 \quad} \times \underline{\quad 25 \quad} = \underline{\quad 150,000 \quad}$

> I could have chosen to round 25 to 30. However, multiplying by 25 is
> mental math for me. If I round 26 to 25, I know my estimated product
> will be closer to the actual product than if I round 26 to 30.

EUREKA
MATH™

Lesson 2:   Estimate multi-digit products by rounding factors to a basic fact and
              using place value patterns.

©2015 Great Minds. eureka-math.org
G5-M1-HWH-1.3.0-07.2015

3

2. There are 6,015 seats available for each of the Radio City Rockettes Spring Spectacular dance shows. If there are a total of 68 shows, about how many tickets are available in all?

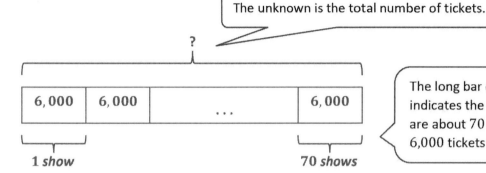

The problem says "about," so I know to estimate.

The unknown is the total number of tickets.

The long bar of the tape diagram indicates the total amount. There are about 70 shows and about 6,000 tickets for each show.

$6,000 \times 70$

$= 6 \text{ thousands} \times 7 \text{ tens} = 42 \text{ ten thousands} = 420,000$

$= (6 \times 7) \times (1,000 \times 10) = 42 \times 10,000 = 420,000$

About 420,000 tickets are available for the shows.

I can think about the problem in more than one way.

EUREKA
MATH

G5-M2-Lesson 3

1. Draw a model. Then write the numerical expression.

   a. The sum of 5 and 4, doubled

   > The directions don't ask me to solve, or evaluate, so I don't have to find the answers.

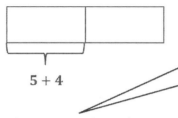

   $5 + 4$

   > I can show doubling by multiplying by 2 or by adding the two sums together. The tape diagram represents both expressions.

   $(5 + 4) \times 2$ *or* $(5 + 4) + (5 + 4)$

   > "The sum of 5 and 4" means 5 and 4 are being added.

   b. 3 times the difference between 42.6 and 23.9

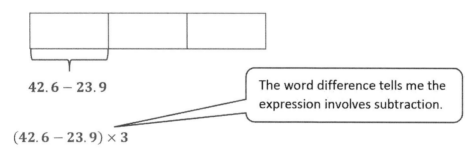

   $42.6 - 23.9$

   > The word difference tells me the expression involves subtraction.

   $(42.6 - 23.9) \times 3$

   c. The sum of 4 twelves and 3 sixes

   > Another way to say 4 *twelves* is to say 4 *groups of twelve.*

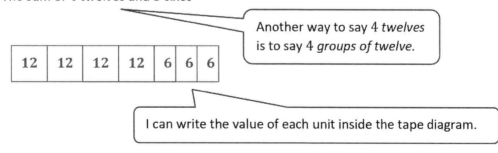

   > I can write the value of each unit inside the tape diagram.

   $(4 \times 12) + (3 \times 6)$ *or* $12 + 12 + 12 + 12 + 6 + 6 + 6$

EUREKA MATH

Lesson 3:   Write and interpret numerical expressions, and compare expressions using a visual model.

©2015 Great Minds. eureka-math.org
G5-M1-HWH-1.3.0-07.2015

5

2. Compare the two expressions using >, <, or =.

a. $(2 \times 3) + (5 \times 3)$ $3 \times (2 + 5)$

> Using the commutative property, I know that 7 threes is equal to 3 sevens.

> I can think of $(2 \times 3) + (5 \times 3)$ in unit form.
> 2 threes + 5 threes = 7 threes = 21.

b. $28 \times (3 + 50)$ $<$ $(3 + 50) \times 82$

> 82 units of fifty-three is more than 28 units of fifty-three.

Lesson 3:   Write and interpret numerical expressions, and compare expressions using a visual model.

©2015 Great Minds. eureka-math.org
G5-M1-HWH-1.3.0-07.2015

EUREKA MATH

G5-M2-Lesson 4

1. Circle each expression that is not equivalent to the expression in **bold**.

    14 × 31

    > I think of this as 14 units of thirty-one.
    > It's like counting by 31's: 31, 62, 93, 124, ..., 434.

    14 thirty-ones   31 fourteens $(13 - 1) \times 31$ $(10 \times 31) - (4 \times 31)$

    > The commutative property says
    > $14 \times 31 = 31 \times 14$, or
    > 14 thirty-ones = 31 fourteens.

    > This would be equivalent if it were $13 + 1$ instead.

    > I think of this as 10 thirty-ones minus 4 thirty-ones. This expression is equal to 6 thirty-ones not 14 thirty-ones.

2. Solve using mental math. Draw a tape diagram and fill in the blanks to show your thinking.

    a. $19 \times 25 = \underline{19}$ twenty-fives

    b. $21 \times 32 = \underline{21}$ thirty-twos

    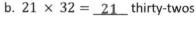

    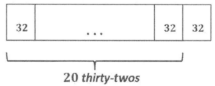
    20 *thirty-twos*

    Think: 20 twenty-fives − 1 twenty-five

    $= (\underline{20} \times 25) - (\underline{1} \times 25)$

    $= \underline{500} - 25 = \underline{475}$

    Think: $\underline{20}$ thirty-twos + $\underline{1}$ thirty-two

    $= (\underline{20} \times 32) + (\underline{1} \times 32)$

    $= \underline{640} + \underline{32} = \underline{672}$

EUREKA MATH™   Lesson 4:   Convert numerical expressions into unit form as a mental strategy for multi-digit multiplication.   7

©2015 Great Minds. eureka-math.org
G5-M1-HWH-1.3.0-07.2015

3. The pet store has 99 fish tanks with 44 fish in each tank. How many fish does the pet store have? Use mental math to solve. Explain your thinking.

I need to find 99 *forty-fours.*

I know that 99 *forty-fours is* 1 *unit of forty-four less than* 100 *forty-fours.*

I multiplied 100 × 44, *which is* 4, 400.

I need to subtract one group of 44.

4, 400 − 44. *The pet store has* 4, 356 *fish.*

8   **Lesson 4:**   Convert numerical expressions into unit form as a mental strategy for multi-
                              digit multiplication.

©2015 Great Minds. eureka-math.org
G5-M1-HWH-1.3.0-07.2015

G5-M2-Lesson 5

1. Draw an area model, and then solve using the standard algorithm. Use arrows to match the partial products from the area model to the partial products in the algorithm.

    a. 33×21

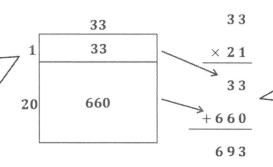

I put the ones on top in the area model so the partial products are in the same order as in the algorithm.

33 and 660 are both *partial products*. I can add them together to find the final *product*.

    b. 433×21

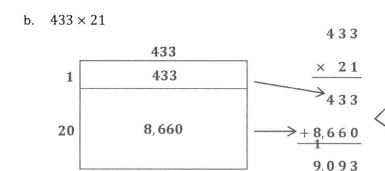

When I add the hundreds in the two partial products, the sum is 10 hundreds, or 1,000. I record the 1 thousand below the partial products, rather than above.

2. Elizabeth pays $123 each month for her cell phone service. How much does she spend in a year?

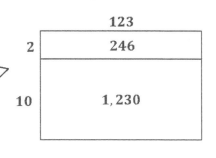

I can draw an area model to help me see where the 2 partial products come from.

Elizabeth spends $1,476 *in a year for cell phone service.*

EUREKA
MATH

Lesson 5:   Multiply decimal fractions with tenths by multi-digit whole numbers using place value understanding to record partial products.

©2015 Great Minds. eureka-math.org
G5-M1-HWH-1.3.0-07.2015

9

G5-M2-Lesson 6

1. Draw an area model. Then, solve using the standard algorithm. Use arrows to match the partial products from your area model to the partial products in the algorithm.

a. 39×45

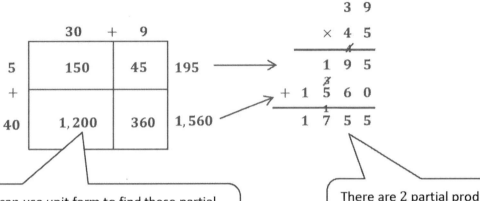

I can use unit form to find these partial products. For example, 3 tens × 4 tens is 12 hundreds or 1,200.

There are 2 partial products in the standard algorithm because I multiplied by 45, a 2-digit factor.

b. 339×45

The area model shows the factors expanded. If I wanted to, I could put the + between the units.

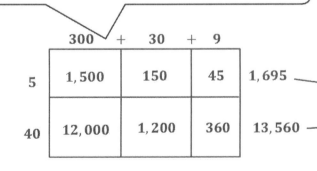

Lesson 6:   Connect area diagrams and the distributive property to partial products of the standard algorithm without renaming.

EUREKA MATH

2. Desmond bought a car and paid monthly installments. Each installment was $452 per month. After 36 months, Desmond still owes $1,567. What was the total price of the car?

> I'll find out how much Desmond would pay in 36 months.

```
      4  5  2
   ×     3  6
   ─────────────
      2  7  1  2
 + 1  3  5  6  0
   ─────────────
   1  6,  2  7  2
```

```
   1  6,  2  7  2
 +    1,  5  6  7
   ───────────────
   1  7,  8  3  9
```

> I'll add what he paid after 36 months to what Desmond still owes.

The total price of the car was $17,839.

> I remembered to write a sentence that answers the question.

EUREKA MATH

Lesson 6: Connect area diagrams and the distributive property to partial products of the standard algorithm without renaming.

11

G5-M2-Lesson 7

1. Draw an area model. Then, solve using the standard algorithm. Use arrows to match the partial products from the area model to the partial products in the algorithm.

$431 \times 246 = \underline{106,026}$

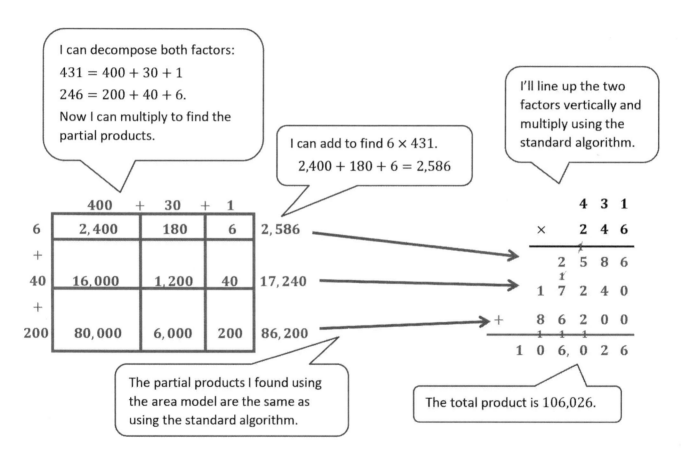

I can decompose both factors:
$431 = 400 + 30 + 1$
$246 = 200 + 40 + 6$.
Now I can multiply to find the partial products.

I can add to find 6×431.
$2,400 + 180 + 6 = 2,586$

I'll line up the two factors vertically and multiply using the standard algorithm.

The partial products I found using the area model are the same as using the standard algorithm.

The total product is 106,026.

Lesson 7:   Connect area models and the distributive property to partial products of the standard algorithm with renaming.

EUREKA MATH

2. Solve by drawing the area model and using the standard algorithm.

$2{,}451 \times 107 = \underline{262{,}257}$

I can decompose 2,451 and use it as the length.
$2{,}451 = 2{,}000 + 400 + 50 + 1$

I multiply to find the partial products.

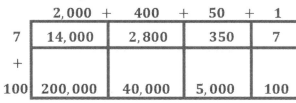

	2,000 +	400 +	50 +	1	
7	14,000	2,800	350	7	17,157
+					
100	200,000	40,000	5,000	100	245,100

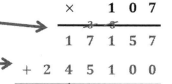

```
      2, 4 5 1
   ×     1 0 7
   ───────────
      1 7 1 5 7
 +  2 4 5 1 0 0
   ───────────
    2 6 2, 2 5 7
```

I decompose the width, 107.
$107 = 100 + 7$
Since there's a 0 in the tens place, there are 0 tens in the width of the area model.

3. Solve using the standard algorithm.

$7{,}302 \times 408 = \underline{2{,}979{,}216}$

8 ones × 3 hundreds = 24 hundreds = 2 thousands 4 hundreds. I'll record 2 in the thousands place and write 4 in the hundreds place.

8 ones × 2 ones = 16 ones = 1 ten 6 ones. I'll record 1 in the tens place and write 6 in the ones place.

```
       7, 3 0 2
    ×      4 0 8
    ───────────
       5 8 4 1 6
 +  2  9 2 0 8 0 0
    ───────────
   2, 9 7 9, 2 1 6
```

4 hundreds × 3 hundreds = 12 ten thousands. I'll record 1 in the hundred thousands place and write 2 in the ten thousands place.

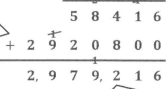

4 hundreds + 8 hundreds = 12 hundreds = 1 thousand 2 hundreds. I'll record 1 in the thousands place and write 2 in the hundreds place.

EUREKA MATH   Lesson 7:   Connect area models and the distributive property to partial products of the standard algorithm with renaming.   13

©2015 Great Minds. eureka-math.org
G5-M1-HWH-1.3.0-07.2015

G5-M2-Lesson 8

1. Estimate the products first. Solve by using the standard algorithm. Use your estimate to check the reasonableness of the product.

   a. 795×248

   $\approx 800 \times 200$

   $= 160,000$

   > I could have rounded 248 to 250 in order to have an estimate that is closer to the actual product. Another reasonable estimate is $800 \times 250 = 200,000$.

   ```
         7  9  5
    ×    2  4  8
    ─────────────
       6  3  6  0
    3  1  8  0  0
  + 1  5  9  0  0  0
  ─────────────────
    1  9  7, 1  6  0
   ```

   > $8 \times 5 = 40$, which I record as 4 tens 0 ones. 8×9 tens $= 72$ tens plus 4 tens, makes 76 tens. I record 76 tens as 7 hundreds 6 tens.

   > This product is reasonable because $197,160$ is close to 160,000. My other estimate is also reasonable because 197,000 is very close to 200,000.

   b. $4,308 \times 505$

   $\approx 4,000 \times 500$

   $= 2,000,000$

   > I have to be careful to estimate accurately. 4 thousands $\times$ 5 hundreds is 20 hundred thousands. That's the same as 2 million. If I just count zeros I might get a wrong estimate.

   ```
          4, 3  0  8
    ×        5  0  5
    ────────────────
       2  1  5  4  0
  + 2  1  5  4  0  0  0
  ─────────────────────
    2, 1  7  5, 5  4  0
   ```

   > This partial product is the result of $5 \times 4,308$.

   > This partial product is the result of $500 \times 4,308$. It makes sense that it is 100 times greater than the first partial product.

2. When multiplying 809 times 528, Isaac got a product of 42,715. Without calculating, does his product seem reasonable? Explain your thinking.

   Isaac's product of about 40 thousands is not reasonable. A correct estimate is 8 hundreds times 5 hundreds, which is 40 ten thousands. That's the same as 400,000 not 40,000.

   > I think Isaac rounded 809 to 800 and 528 to 500. Then, I think he multiplied 8 times 5 to get 40. From there, I think he miscounted the zeros.

Fluently multiply multi-digit whole numbers using the standard algorithm and using estimation to check for reasonableness of the product.   **EUREKA MATH**

G5-M2-Lesson 9

Solve.

1. Howard and Robin are both cabinet makers. Over the last year, Howard made 107 cabinets. Robin made 28 more cabinets than Howard. Each cabinet they make has exactly 102 nails in it. How many nails did they use altogether while making the cabinets?

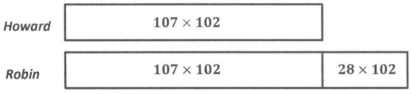

> Although there are several steps to calculate, the question mark goes here, because this is what the problem is asking.

Howard	107×102	
Robin	107×102	28×102

?

> Once I know how many cabinets Robin and Howard made, I can multiply by the number of nails that were used (102).

Howard:

```
      1 0 7
  ×   1 0 2
  ─────────
      2 1 4
+ 1 0 7 0 0
  ─────────
  1 0, 9 1 4
```

Robin: $107 + 28 = 135$

```
      1 3 5
  ×   1 0 2
  ─────────
      2 7 0
+ 1 3 5 0 0
  ─────────
  1 3, 7 7 0
```

```
  1 0, 9 1 4
+ 1 3, 7 7 0
  ─────────
  2 4, 6 8 4
```

> 9 hundreds plus 7 hundreds is equal to 16 hundreds. I'll record 1 in the thousands place and write 6 in the hundreds place.

Together they used 24, 684 *nails.*

EUREKA MATH Lesson 9: Fluently multiply multi-digit whole numbers using the standard algorithm to solve multi-step word problems.   15

©2015 Great Minds. eureka-math.org
G5-M1-HWH-1.3.0-07.2015

2. Mrs. Peterson made 32 car payments at $533 each. She still owes $8,530 on her car. How much did the car cost?

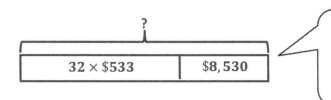

?

| 32 × $533 | $8,530 |

My tape diagram shows two parts: 32 payments at $533 and the $8,530 she still owes. All I have to do is find both parts and then add!

```
      5 3 3
  ×     3 2
  ─────────
    1 0 6 6
+ 1 5 9 9 0
   1  1
  ─────────
  1 7, 0 5 6
```

```
    1 7, 0 5 6
  +   8, 5 3 0
      1
  ───────────
    2 5, 5 8 6
```

Mrs. Peterson's car cost $25,586.

EUREKA MATH

G5-M2-Lesson 10

1. Estimate the product. Solve using an area model and the standard algorithm. Remember to express your products in standard form.

> I rename 4.1 as 41 tenths and then multiply.

> I round 23 to the nearest ten, 2 tens, and 4.1 to the nearest one, 4 ones.

$$23 \times 4.1 \approx \underline{\quad 20 \quad} \times \underline{\quad 4 \quad} = \underline{\quad 80 \quad}$$

> 2 tens × 4 ones = 8 tens, or 80. This is the estimated product.

```
        2  3
    ×   4  1   (tenths)
    ─────────────
        2  3
  +  9  2  0
    ─────────────
     9  4  3   (tenths) = 94.3
```

> 943 tenths, or 94.3, is the actual product, which is close to my estimated product of 80.

> I decompose 23 to 20 + 3, and 41 tenths to 40 tenths + 1 tenth.

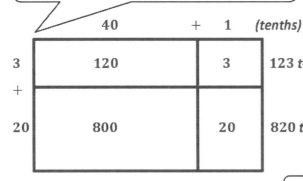

	40	+ 1	(tenths)
3	120	3	123 *tenths*
+ 20	800	20	820 *tenths*

> 120 tenths + 3 tenths = 123 tenths.

> 800 tenths + 20 tenths = 820 tenths.

> 123 tenths + 820 tenths = 943 tenths, or 94.3.

EUREKA MATH™   Lesson 10:   Multiply decimal fractions with tenths by multi-digit whole numbers using place value understanding to record partial products.   17

©2015 Great Minds. eureka-math.org
G5-M1-HWH-1.3.0-07.2015

2. Estimate. Then, use the standard algorithm to solve. Express your products in standard form.

I round 7.1 to the nearest one, 7 ones, and 29 to the nearest ten, 3 tens.

a. $7.1 \times 29 \approx$ ___7___ $\times$ ___30___ $=$ ___210___

7 ones × 3 tens = 21 tens, or 210. This is the estimated product.

$$
\begin{array}{r}
7\ \ 1\ \ \text{(tenths)} \\
\times\ \ 2\ \ 9 \\
\hline
6\ \ 3\ \ 9 \\
+\ 1\ \ 4\ \ 2\ \ 0 \\
\hline
2,\ 0\ \ 5\ \ 9\ \ \text{(tenths)} = 205.9
\end{array}
$$

2,059 tenths, or 205.9, is the actual product, which is close to my estimated product of 210.

I round 182.4 to the nearest hundreds, 2 hundreds, and 32 to the nearest tens, 3 tens.

b. $182.4 \times 32 \approx$ ___200___ $\times$ ___30___ $=$ ___6,000___

2 hundreds × 3 tens = 6 thousandths, or 6,000. This is the estimated product.

$$
\begin{array}{r}
1\ \ 8\ \ 2\ \ 4\ \ \text{(tenths)} \\
\times\ \ \ \ \ \ 3\ \ 2 \\
\hline
3\ \ 6\ \ 4\ \ 8 \\
+\ 5\ \ 4\ \ 7\ \ 2\ \ 0 \\
\hline
5\ \ 8,\ 3\ \ 6\ \ 8\ \ \text{(tenths)}\ = 5,836.8
\end{array}
$$

58,368 tenths, or 5,836.8, is the actual product, which is close to my estimated product of 6,000.

Lesson 10: Multiply decimal fractions with tenths by multi-digit whole numbers using place value understanding to record partial products.

EUREKA MATH

©2015 Great Minds. eureka-math.org
G5-M1-HWH-1.3.0-07.2015

G5-M2-Lesson 11

1. Estimate the product. Solve using the standard algorithm. Use the thought bubbles to show your thinking.

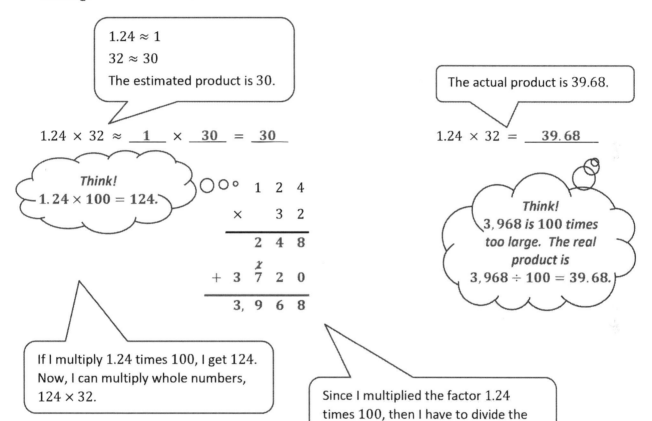

1.24 ≈ 1
32 ≈ 30
The estimated product is 30.

$1.24 \times 32 \approx$ __1__ $\times$ __30__ = __30__

The actual product is 39.68.

$1.24 \times 32 =$ __39.68__

Think!
$1.24 \times 100 = 124.$

$$\begin{array}{r} 1\ 2\ 4 \\ \times\quad\ \ 3\ 2 \\ \hline 2\ 4\ 8 \\ +\ \ 3\ 7\ 2\ 0 \\ \hline 3,\ 9\ 6\ 8 \end{array}$$

Think!
3, 968 *is 100 times too large. The real product is*
$3,968 \div 100 = 39.68.$

If I multiply 1.24 times 100, I get 124.
Now, I can multiply whole numbers,
124×32.

Since I multiplied the factor 1.24 times 100, then I have to divide the product by 100. The answer is 39.68.

EUREKA
MATH

Lesson 11:   Multiply decimal fractions by multi-digit whole numbers through
conversion to a whole number problem and reasoning about the
placement of the decimal.

©2015 Great Minds. eureka-math.org
G5-M1-HWH-1.3.0-07.2015

19

2. Solve using the standard algorithm.

2.46×132

$= 324.72$

$$
\begin{array}{r}
2\ 4\ 6 \\
\times\ \ 1\ 3\ 2 \\
\hline
4\ 9\ 2 \\
7\ 3\ 8\ 0 \\
+\ 2\ 4\ 6\ 0\ 0 \\
\hline
3\ 2\ 4\ 7\ 2
\end{array}
$$

> 2.46 times 100 is equal to 246. Now, I can multiply 246 times 132.

> I have to remember to divide the product by 100.
> $32{,}472 \div 100 = 324.72$

3. Use the whole number product and place value reasoning to place the decimal point in the second product. Explain how you know.

If $54 \times 736 = 39{,}744$,   then $54 \times 7.36 = \underline{\ 397.44\ }$.

> I can compare the factors in both number sentences. Since $736 \div 100 = 7.36$, then I can divide the product by 100.

7.36 is 736 hundredths, so I can just divide 39,744 by 100.

$39{,}744 \div 100 = 397.44$

Lesson 11: Multiply decimal fractions by multi-digit whole numbers through conversion to a whole number problem and reasoning about the placement of the decimal.

©2015 Great Minds. eureka-math.org
G5-M1-HWH-1.3.0-07.2015

EUREKA MATH

G5-M2-Lesson 12

1. Estimate. Then solve using the standard algorithm. You may draw an area model if it helps you.

$14 \times 3.12 \approx$ ___10___ $\times$ ___3___ $=$ ___30___

$$
\begin{array}{r}
3.\ 1\ 2 \\
\times \quad 1\ 4 \\
\hline
1\ 2\ 4\ 8 \\
+\ 3\ 1\ 2\ 0 \\
\hline
4\ 3.\ 6\ 8
\end{array}
$$

> $14 \approx 10$
> $3.12 \approx 3$
> The estimated product is 30.

> I have to remember to write the product as a number of hundredths.

> I'll decompose 14 as $10 + 4$, and 312 hundredths as 300 hundredths + 10 hundredths + 2 hundredths.

> 1,200 hundredths + 40 hundredths + 8 hundredths = 1,248 hundredths.

	300 +	10 +	2 *(hundredths)*	
4	1,200	40	8	1,248 *hundredths*
+				
10	3,000	100	20	3,120 *hundredths*

> 3,000 hundredths + 100 hundredths + 20 hundredths = 3,120 hundredths.

> 1,248 hundredths + 3,120 hundredths = 4,368 hundredths, or 43.68.

EUREKA MATH   **Lesson 12:**   Reason about the product of a whole number and a decimal with hundredths using place value understanding and estimation.   **21**

©2015 Great Minds. eureka-math.org
G5-M1-HWH-1.3.0-07.2015

2. Estimate. Then solve using the standard algorithm.

a. $0.47 \times 32 \approx$ ___0.5___ $\times$ ___30___ $=$ ___15___

> $0.47 \approx 0.5$
> $32 \approx 30$
> Multiplying 0.5 times 30 is the same as taking half of 30. The estimated product is 15.

> I'll think of multiplying $0.47 \times 100 = 47$. Now, I'll think of multiplying 47 times 32.

$$
\begin{array}{r}
0.\,4\ 7 \\
\times \quad 3\ 2 \\
\hline
9\ 4 \\
+\ 1\ 4\ 1\ 0 \\
\hline
1\ 5.\,0\ 4 \\
\end{array}
$$

> I have to remember to write the product as a number of hundredths. $1{,}504 \div 100 = 15.04$.

b. $6.04 \times 307 \approx$ ___6___ $\times$ ___300___ $=$ ___1,800___

> $6.04 \approx 6$
> $307 \approx 300$
> 6 ones times 3 hundreds is equal to 18 hundreds, or 1,800.

$$
\begin{array}{r}
6.\,0\ 4 \\
\times\ 3\ 0\ 7 \\
\hline
4\ 2\ 2\ 8 \\
+\ 1\ 8\ 1\ 2\ 0\ 0 \\
\hline
1{,}\ 8\ 5\ 4.\,2\ 8 \\
\end{array}
$$

> The actual product is 1,854.28, which is very close to my estimated product of 1,800.

3. Tatiana walks to the park every afternoon. In the month of August, she walked 2.35 miles each day. How far did Tatiana walk during the month of August?

There are 31 days in August.

Tatiana walked 72.85 miles in August.

> I'll multiply 2.35 times 31 days to find the total distance Tatiana walks during the month of August.

$$
\begin{array}{r}
2.\,3\ 5 \\
\times \quad 3\ 1 \\
\hline
2\ 3\ 5 \\
+\ 7\ 0\ 5\ 0 \\
\hline
7\ 2.\,8\ 5 \\
\end{array}
$$

Lesson 12:   Reason about the product of a whole number and a decimal with hundredths using place value understanding and estimation.

EUREKA MATH

©2015 Great Minds. eureka-math.org
G5-M1-HWH-1.3.0-07.2015

G5-M2-Lesson 13

1. Solve.

   a. Convert years to days.

   $5 \text{ years} = 5 \times (1 \text{ year})$

   $\qquad\qquad = 5 \times (365 \text{ days})$

   $\qquad\qquad = 1,825 \text{ days}$

   $$\begin{array}{r} 3 \ 6 \ 5 \\ \times \qquad 5 \\ \hline 1, \ 8 \ 2 \ 5 \end{array}$$

   > 1 year is equal to 365 days. I can multiply 5 times 365 days to find 1,825 days in 5 years.

   b. Convert pounds to ounces.

   $13.5 \text{ lb.} = 13.5 \times (1 \text{ lb.})$

   $\qquad\qquad = 13.5 \times (16 \text{ oz.})$

   $\qquad\qquad = 216 \text{ oz.}$

   $$\begin{array}{r} 1 \ 3. \ 5 \\ \times \quad 1 \ 6 \\ \hline 8 \ 1 \ 0 \\ + \ 1 \ 3 \ 5 \ 0 \\ \hline 2 \ 1 \ 6. \ 0 \end{array}$$

   > 1 pound is equal to 16 ounces. I can multiply 13.5 times 16 ounces to find that there are 216 ounces in 13.5 pounds.

2. After solving, write a statement to express each conversion.

   a. The height of a male ostrich is 7.3 meters. What is his height in centimeters?

   $7.3 \text{ m} = 7.3 \times (1 \text{ m})$

   $\qquad\qquad = 7.3 \times (100 \text{ cm})$

   $\qquad\qquad = 730 \text{ cm}$

   > 1 meter is equal to 100 centimeters. I multiply 7.3 times 100 centimeters to get 730 centimeters.

   His height is 730 centimeters.

b. The capacity of a container is 0.3 liter. Convert this to milliliters.

$$0.3 \text{ L} = 0.3 \times (1 \text{ L})$$
$$= 0.3 \times (1{,}000 \text{ ml})$$
$$= 300 \text{ ml}$$

1 liter is equal to 1,000 milliliters. I multiply 0.3 times 1,000 milliliters to get 300 milliliters.

The capacity of the container is 300 milliliters.

EUREKA
MATH

G5-M2-Lesson 14

1. Solve.

   a. Convert quarts to gallons.

      $28 \text{ quarts} = 28 \times (\mathbf{1 \text{ quart}})$

      $\qquad\qquad\quad = 28 \times \left(\frac{1}{4} \text{ gallon}\right)$

      $\qquad\qquad\quad = \frac{28}{4} \text{ gallons}$

      $\qquad\qquad\quad = 7 \text{ gallons}$

      > 1 quart is equal to $\frac{1}{4}$ gallon. I multiply 28 times $\frac{1}{4}$ gallon to find 7 gallons is equal to 28 quarts.

   b. Convert grams to kilograms.

      $5{,}030 \text{ g} = 5{,}030 \times (\mathbf{1 \text{ g}})$

      $\qquad\qquad = 5{,}030 \times (\mathbf{0.001 \text{ kg}})$

      $\qquad\qquad = 5.030 \text{ kg}$

      > 1 gram is equal to 0.001 kilogram. I multiply 5,030 times 0.001 kilogram to get 5.030 kilograms.

2. After solving, write a statement to express each conversion.

   a. A jug of milk holds 16 cups. Convert 16 cups to pints.

      $16 \text{ cups} = 16 \times (\mathbf{1 \text{ cup}})$

      $\qquad\qquad = 16 \times \left(\frac{1}{2} \text{ pint}\right)$

      $\qquad\qquad = \frac{16}{2} \text{ pints}$

      $\qquad\qquad = 8 \text{ pints}$

      > 1 cup is equal to $\frac{1}{2}$ pint. I multiply 16 times $\frac{1}{2}$ pint to find that 8 pints is equal to 16 cups.

      16 cups is equal to 8 pints.

   b. The length of a table is 305 centimeters. What is its length in meters?

      $305 \text{ cm} = 305 \times (\mathbf{1 \text{ cm}})$

      $\qquad\qquad = 305 \times (\mathbf{0.01 \text{ m}})$

      $\qquad\qquad = 3.05 \text{ m}$

      > 1 centimeter is equal to 0.01 meter. I multiply 305 times 0.01 meter to get 3.05 meters.

      The table's length is 3.05 meters.

G5-M2-Lesson 15

1. A bag of peanuts is 5 times as heavy as a bag of sunflower seeds. The bag of peanuts also weighs 920 grams more than the bag of sunflower seeds.

   a. What is the total weight in grams for the bag of peanuts and the bag of sunflower seeds?

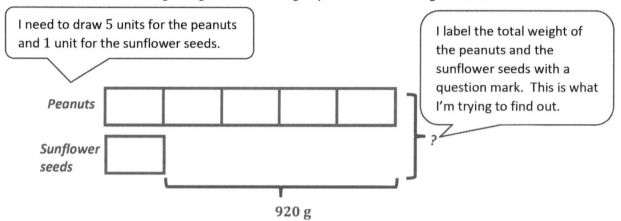

I need to draw 5 units for the peanuts and 1 unit for the sunflower seeds.

I label the total weight of the peanuts and the sunflower seeds with a question mark. This is what I'm trying to find out.

920 g

Since I know 4 units is equal to 920 grams, I'll divide 920 grams by 4 to find the value of 1 unit, which is equal to 230 grams.

$$4 \text{ units} = 920 \text{ g}$$
$$1 \text{ unit} = 920 \text{ g} \div 4$$
$$= 230 \text{ g}$$

```
        2  3  0
   4 | 9  2  0
     -  8
     ─────────
        1  2
      -  1  2
      ─────────
           0  0
         -    0
      ─────────
              0
```

There are a total of 6 units between the peanuts and the sunflower seeds. I multiply 6 times 230 grams to get a total of 1,380 grams.

$$6 \text{ units} = 6 \times 230 \text{ g}$$
$$= 1,380 \text{ g}$$

```
     2  3  0
  ×        6
  ──────────
  1, 3  8  0
```

The total weight for the bag of peanuts and the bag of sunflower seeds is 1,380 grams.

EUREKA MATH™

b. Express the total weight of the bag of peanuts and the bag of sunflower seeds in kilograms.

$1,380 \text{ g} = 1,380 \times (1 \text{ g})$

$\qquad = 1,380 \times (0.001 \text{ kg})$

$\qquad = 1.380 \text{ kg}$

> 1 gram is equal to 0.001 kilogram. I multiply 1,380 times 0.001 kilogram to find that 1.38 kilograms is equal to 1,380 grams.

The total weight of the bag of peanuts and the bag of sunflower seeds is 1.38 kilograms.

> 4 meters 50 centimeters is equal to 450 centimeters.

2. Gabriel cut a 4 meter 50 centimeter string into 9 equal pieces. Michael cut a 508 centimeter string into 10 equal pieces. How much longer is one of Michael's strings than one of Gabriel's?

Gabriel: $450 \text{ cm} \div 9 = 50 \text{ cm}$

> Each piece of Gabriel's string is 50 centimeters long.

Michael: $508 \text{ cm} \div 10 = 50.8 \text{ cm}$

> Each piece of Michael's string is 50.8 centimeters long.

$50.8 \text{ cm} - 50 \text{ cm} = 0.8 \text{ cm}$

> I'll subtract to find the difference between Michael and Gabriel's strings.

One of Michael's strings is 0.8 centimeters longer than one of Gabriel's.

G5-M2-Lesson 16

1. Divide. Draw place value disks to show your thinking for (a).

   a. $400 \div 10 = 40$

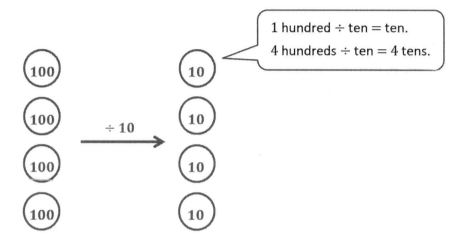

1 hundred ÷ ten = ten.

4 hundreds ÷ ten = 4 tens.

   b. $650,000 \div 100$

   $= 6,500 \div 1$

   $= 6,500$

   I can divide both the dividend and the divisor by 100, so I can rewrite the division sentence as $6,500 \div 1$. The answer is 6,500.

Dividing by 40 is the same thing as dividing by 10 and then dividing by 4.

2. Divide.

   a. $240,000 \div 40$

   $= 240,000 \div 10 \div 4$

   $= 24,000 \div 4$

   $= 6,000$

   I can solve $240,000 \div 10 = 24,000$. Then I can find that $24,000 \div 4 = 6,000$.

   In unit form, this is 24 thousands ÷ 4 = 6 thousands.

Lesson 16:   Use divide by 10 patterns for multi-digit whole number division.

©2015 Great Minds. eureka-math.org
G5-M1-HWH-1.3.0-07.2015

b. $240,000 \div 400$

$= 240,000 \div 100 \div 4$

> Dividing by 400 is the same thing as dividing by 100 and then dividing by 4.

$= 2,400 \div 4$

$= 600$

> I can solve $240,000 \div 100 = 2,400$. Then I can solve $2,400 \div 4 = 600$.

> Dividing by 4,000 is the same thing as dividing by 1,000 and then dividing by 4.

c. $240,000 \div 4,000$

$= 240,000 \div 1,000 \div 4$

$= 240 \div 4$

$= 60$

> I can solve $240,000 \div 1,000 = 240$. Then I can solve $240 \div 4 = 60$.

©2015 Great Minds. eureka-math.org
G5-M1-HWH-1.3.0-07.2015

G5-M2-Lesson 17

1. Estimate the quotient for the following problems.

a. $612 \div 33$

> I look at the divisor, 33, and round it to the nearest ten. $33 \approx 30$

$\approx 600 \div 30$

> I need to think of a multiple of 30 that's closest to 612. 600 works.

$= 20$

> I use the simple fact, $6 \div 3 = 2$, to help me solve $600 \div 30 = 20$.

b. $735 \div 78$

> I look at the divisor, 78, and round it to the nearest ten. $78 \approx 80$

$\approx 720 \div 80$

> I'll think of a multiple of 80 that is close to 735. 720 is the closest multiple.

$= 9$

> I use the simple fact, $72 \div 8 = 9$, to help me solve $720 \div 80 = 9$.

c. $821 \div 99$

> I look at the divisor, 99, and round to the nearest ten. $99 \approx 100$

$\approx 800 \div 100$

> I can think of a multiple of 100 that is close to 821. 800 is the closest multiple.

$= 8$

> I can use the simple fact, $8 \div 1 = 8$, to help solve $800 \div 100 = 8$.

©2015 Great Minds. eureka-math.org
G5-M1-HWH-1.3.0-07.2015

2. A baker spent \$989 buying 48 pounds of nuts. About how much does each pound of nuts cost?

> To find the cost of 1 pound of nuts, I'll use division. $989 \div 48$

$989 \div 48$

> I look at the divisor, 48, and round it to the nearest ten. $48 \approx 50$

$\approx 1,000 \div 50$

> I need to think of a multiple of 50 that's close to 989. 1,000 is closest.

$= 20$

> I can use the simple fact, $10 \div 5 = 2$, to help me solve $1,000 \div 50 = 20$.

Each pound of nuts costs about \$20.

G5-M2-Lesson 18

1. Estimate the quotients for the following problems.

> I look at the divisor, 23, and round it to the nearest ten. $23 \approx 20$

a. $3,782 \div 23$

$\approx 4,000 \div 20$

> I need to think of a multiple of 20 that's closest to 3,782. 4,000 is closest.

$= 200$

> I use the simple fact, $4 \div 2 = 2$, and unit form to help me solve.
> 4 thousands $\div$ 2 tens = 2 hundreds

> I look at the divisor, 43, and round to the nearest ten. $43 \approx 40$

b. $2,519 \div 43$

$\approx 2,400 \div 40$

> I need to think of a multiple of 40 that's close to 2,519. 2,400 is closest.

$= 60$

> I can use the simple fact, $24 \div 4 = 6$, to help me solve $2,400 \div 40 = 60$.

> I look at the divisor, 94, and round it to the nearest ten. $94 \approx 90$

c. $4,621 \div 94$

$\approx 4,500 \div 90$

> 4,500 is close to 4,621 and is a multiple of 90.

$= 50$

> I can use the simple fact, $45 \div 9 = 5$, to help me solve $4,500 \div 90 = 50$.

Lesson 18:   Use basic facts to approximate quotients with two-digit divisors.   **EUREKA MATH**

©2015 Great Minds. eureka-math.org
G5-M1-HWH-1.3.0-07.2015

2. Meilin has saved \$4,825. If she is paid \$68 an hour, about how many hours did she work?

I'll use division to find the number of hours that Meilin worked to save \$4,825.

The divisor, 68, rounds to 70. $68 \approx 70$

$4,825 \div 68$

$\approx 4,900 \div 70$

I need to find a multiple of 70 that's closest to 4,825. 4,900 is closest.

$= 70$

I can use the basic fact, $49 \div 7 = 7$, to help me solve $4,900 \div 70 = 70$.

Meilin worked about 70 hours.

G5-M2-Lesson 19

1. Divide, and then check.

a. $87 \div 40$

> I use the estimation strategy from the previous lesson to help me solve.
> $80 \div 40 = 2$. The estimated quotient is 2.

> I write the remainder of 7 here next to the quotient of 2.

> I check my answer by multiplying the divisor of 40 by the quotient of 2 and then add the remainder of 7.

```
       2  R 7
40 | 8 7
  -  8 0
       7
```

> 2 groups of 40 is equal to 80.

Check:

$40 \times 2 = 80$

$80 + 7 = 87$

> The difference between 87 and 80 is 7.

> This 87 matches the original dividend in the problem, which means I divided correctly. The quotient is 2 with a remainder of 7.

b. $451 \div 70$

> I estimate to find the quotient. $420 \div 70 = 6$

> The quotient is 6 with a remainder of 31.

> After checking, I see that 451 does match the original dividend in the problem.

```
          6  R 31
70 | 4 5 1
  -  4 2 0
       3 1
```

Check:

$70 \times 6 = 420$

$420 + 31 = 451$

> The quotient is 6 with a remainder of 31.

Lesson 19:   Divide two- and three-digit dividends by multiples of 10 with single-digit
                          quotients, and make connections to a written method.

EUREKA
MATH™

©2015 Great Minds. eureka-math.org
G5-M1-HWH-1.3.0-07.2015

2. How many groups of thirty are in two hundred twenty-four?

> I use division to find how many 30's are in 224. But first, I estimate to find the quotient. $210 \div 30 = 7$

> There are 7 groups of thirty in 224 with a remainder of 14.

```
        7   R 14
30 | 2 2 4
 -   2 1 0
     1 4
```

> 14 is remaining. In order to make another group of 30, there would need to be 16 more in the dividend, 224.

There are 7 groups of thirty in two hundred twenty-four.

EUREKA MATH   Lesson 19:   Divide two- and three-digit dividends by multiples of 10 with single-digit quotients, and make connections to a written method.   35

©2015 Great Minds. eureka-math.org
G5-M1-HWH-1.3.0-07.2015

G5-M2-Lesson 20

1. Divide. Then check with multiplication.

a. $48 \div 21$

I do a quick mental estimation to find the quotient.
$40 \div 20 = 2$

The actual quotient is 2 with a remainder of 6.

```
      2  R 6
21 | 4 8
  -  4 2
       6
```

I'll check my answer by multiplying the divisor and the quotient, 21×2. Then, I'll add the remainder of 6.

Check:

```
    2 1          4 2
  ×   2        +   6
  ─────        ─────
    4 2          4 8
```

This 48 matches the original dividend in the problem, which means I divided correctly. The quotient is 2 with a remainder of 6.

b. $79 \div 38$

I do a quick mental estimation to find the quotient.
$80 \div 40 = 2$

```
      2  R 3
38 | 7 9
  -  7 6
       3
```

The actual quotient is 2 with a remainder of 3.

Check:

```
    3 8          7 6
  ×   2        +   3
  ─────        ─────
    7 6          7 9
```

After checking, I see that 79 does match the original dividend.

Lesson 20:   Divide two- and three-digit dividends by two-digit divisors with single-digit quotients, and make connections to a written method.

©2015 Great Minds. eureka-math.org
G5-M1-HWH-1.3.0-07.2015

EUREKA MATH

Area is equal to length times width. So, I can use the area divided by the length to find the width.

$$A = l \times w \qquad \text{and} \qquad A \div l = w$$

2. A rectangular 95-square-foot vegetable garden has a length of 19 feet. What is the width of the vegetable garden?

$$95 \div 19 = 5$$

I'll do a quick mental estimation to help me solve.

$$100 \div 20 = 5$$

The quotient of 5 means the width is 5 feet, with 0 feet remaining.

```
        5
  19 | 9 5
    -  9 5
        0
```

The width of the vegetable garden is 5 feet.

3. A number divided by 41 has a quotient of 4 with 15 as a remainder. Find the number.

In other words, 4 units of 41, plus 15 more, is equal to what number?

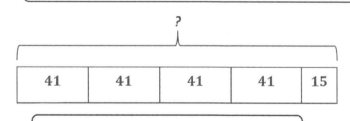

```
     4   R 15
 41 | ?
```

I know I have to find the missing dividend.

I need to add 164 and the remainder of 15 to get a total of 179. The dividend is 179.

I can multiply the divisor of 41 and the quotient of 4 to get 164.

```
      4 1              1 6 4
  ×     4          +     1 5
    1 6 4              1 7 9
```

The number is 179.

EUREKA MATH   Lesson 20:   Divide two- and three-digit dividends by two-digit divisors with single-digit quotients, and make connections to a written method.   37

©2015 Great Minds. eureka-math.org
G5-M1-HWH-1.3.0-07.2015

G5-M2-Lesson 21

1. Divide. Then check using multiplication.

a. $235 \div 68$

> I can find the estimated quotient and then divide using the long division algorithm.

> I can estimate to find the quotient. $210 \div 70 = 3$

> I'll use the quotient of 3. 3 groups of 68 is 204, and the difference between 235 and 204 is 31. The remainder is 31.

```
        3  R 31
68 | 2 3 5
  -  2 0 4
       3 1
```

Check:

```
     6 8
  ×      3
  ─────────
   2 0 4
```

```
   2 0 4
 +    3 1
 ─────────
   2 3 5
```

> After checking, I see that 235 does match the original dividend in the problem.

> I estimate to find the quotient. $120 \div 30 = 4$. Therefore, there should be about 4 units of 32 in 125.

b. $125 \div 32$

> When I use the estimated quotient of 4, I see that 4 groups of 32 is 128. 128 is more than the original dividend of 125. That means I over estimated. The quotient of 4 is too high.

```
        4
32 | 1 2 5
  -  1 2 8
       ?
```

⟹

```
        3  R 29
32 | 1 2 5
  -    9 6
       2 9
```

> Since the quotient of 4 is too much, I'll try 3 as the quotient. 3 groups of 32 is 96. The difference between 125 and 96 is 29. The remainder is 29.

> The actual quotient is 3 with a remainder of 29.

Lesson 21: Divide two- and three-digit dividends by two-digit divisors with single-digit quotients, and make connections to a written method.

EUREKA MATH

©2015 Great Minds. eureka-math.org
G5-M1-HWH-1.3.0-07.2015

Check: ◁──── To check, I'll multiply the divisor and the quotient and then add the remainder.

```
      3  2                         9  6
   ×     3                    +    2  9
   ─────────                  ─────────────
      9  6                       1  2  5
```

I can use division to find how many 49's are in 159. First, I should estimate to find the quotient.
$150 \div 50 = 3$

2. How many forty-nines are in one hundred fifty-nine?

```
           3   R 12
   49 │ 1  5  9
    −   1  4  7
   ─────────────
           1  2
```

There are 3 groups of forty-nine in 159, with a remainder of 12.

12 is the remainder, and it will need 37 more to make another group of 49.

There are 3 groups of forty-nine in 159.

EUREKA
MATH™

Lesson 21:   Divide two- and three-digit dividends by two-digit divisors with single-digit quotients, and make connections to a written method.   39

©2015 Great Minds. eureka-math.org
G5-M1-HWH-1.3.0-07.2015

G5-M2-Lesson 22

1. Divide. Then check using multiplication.

    a. $874 \div 41$

> I look at the dividend of 874 and estimate 80 tens ÷ 40 = 2 tens, or 800 ÷ 40 = 20. I'll record 2 in the tens place. 5 tens remain.

> I look at 54 and estimate 40 ones ÷ 40 = 1 one, or 40 ÷ 40 = 1. I'll record 1 in the ones place. There's a remainder of 13.

```
       2                          2  1   R 13
 41 | 8 7 4                 41 | 8 7 4
   -  8 2                      -  8 2
 ─────────                    ─────────
       5                          5 4
                               -  4 1
                              ─────────
                                  1 3
```

> 5 tens plus 4 in the dividend makes 54.

> The quotient is 21 with a remainder of 13.

Check:

> I check my answer by multiplying the quotient and the divisor, 21×41, and then add the remainder of 13.

```
       2 1
    ×  4 1
   ────────
       2 1
   + 8 4 0
   ────────
     8 6 1
```

```
     8 6 1
   +   1 3
   ────────
     8 7 4
```

> After checking, I get 874, which does match the original dividend. So, I know I solved correctly.

    b. $703 \div 29$

> I look at the dividend of 703 and estimate 60 tens ÷ 30 = 2 tens, or 600 ÷ 30 = 20. I'll record 2 in the tens place. There's a remainder of 12 tens.

```
       2                          2 4   R 7
 29 | 7 0 3                 29 | 7 0 3
   -  5 8                      -  5 8
 ─────────                    ─────────
     1 2                        1 2 3
                              -  1 1 6
                              ─────────
                                    7
```

> I can estimate. 12 tens ÷ 30 = 4 ones, or 120 ÷ 30 = 4. I'll record 4 in the ones place. 4 units of 29 is 116.

> 12 tens plus 3 in the dividend makes 123.

Lesson 22:   Divide three- and four-digit dividends by two-digit divisors resulting in two- and three-digit quotients, reasoning about the decomposition of successive remainders in each place value.

©2015 Great Minds. eureka-math.org
G5-M1-HWH-1.3.0-07.2015

EUREKA MATH

Check: I check my answer by multiplying the quotient and the divisor, and then I add the remainder.

```
    2 4          6 9 6
  × 2 9        +   0 7
  -------      -------
  2 1 6        7 0 3
+ 4 8 0
-------
  6 9 6
```

2. 31 students are selling cupcakes. There are 167 cupcakes to be shared equally among students.

a. How many cupcakes are left over after sharing them equally?

```
         5  R 12
    31 | 1 6 7
     -   1 5 5
         -----
           1 2
```

167 cupcakes shared equally among 31 students: each student gets 5 cupcakes, with 12 cupcakes left over.

There are 12 cupcakes left over after sharing them equally.

b. If each student needs 6 cupcakes to sell, how many more cupcakes are needed?

```
      3 1              7  16
    ×   6           1  8  6
    -----         -  1  6  7
    1 8 6           --------
                      1   9
```

Since each student needs 6 cupcakes, then 31 students will need a total of 186 cupcakes.

The difference between 167 and 186 is 19.

19 more cupcakes are needed.

My solution makes sense. The remainder of 12 cupcakes, in part (a), tells me that if there were 19 more cupcakes, there would be enough for each student to have 6 cupcakes.

$12 + 19 = 31$

EUREKA MATH   Lesson 22: Divide three- and four-digit dividends by two-digit divisors resulting in two- and three-digit quotients, reasoning about the decomposition of successive remainders in each place value.   41

©2015 Great Minds. eureka-math.org
G5-M1-HWH-1.3.0-07.2015

G5-M2-Lesson 23

1. Divide. Then check using multiplication.

   a. $4,753 \div 22$

> I look at the dividend of 4,753 and estimate. 40 hundreds ÷ 20 = 2 hundreds, or 4,000 ÷ 20 = 200. I record 2 in the hundreds place. There's a remainder of 3 hundreds.

> I look at 35 tens and estimate 20 tens ÷ 20 = 1 ten, or 200 ÷ 20 = 10. I record 1 in the tens place. There's a remainder of 13 tens.

> I look at 133 ones and estimate 120 ones ÷ 20 = 6 ones, or 120 ÷ 20 = 6. I record 6 in the ones place. There's a remainder of 1 one.

```
          2                          2   1                      2   1   6   R 1
22 | 4,  7   5   3          22 | 4,  7   5   3          22 | 4,  7   5   3
  -    4   4                   -    4   4                   -    4   4
  ─────────                    ─────────                    ─────────
          3                            3   5                        3   5
                                  -    2   2                   -    2   2
                                  ─────────                    ─────────
                                       1   3                        1   3   3
                                                              -    1   3   2
                                                              ─────────────
                                                                           1
```

> I check my answer by multiplying the quotient and the divisor, 216×22, and then add the remainder of 1.

Check:

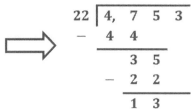

```
      2  1  6
   ×     2  2
   ─────────────
      4  3  2
   + 4  3  2  0
   ─────────────
   4,  7  5  2
```

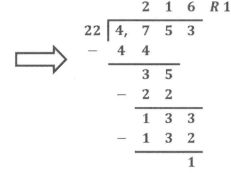

```
   4,  7  5  2
 +           1
 ─────────────
   4,  7  5  3
```

> After checking, I get 4,753, which does match the original dividend. So I know I solved it correctly.

Lesson 23: Divide three- and four-digit dividends by two-digit divisors resulting in two- and three-digit quotients, reasoning about the decomposition of successive remainders in each place value.

©2015 Great Minds. eureka-math.org
G5-M1-HWH-1.3.0-07.2015

EUREKA MATH

I look at the dividend of 3,795 and estimate 360 tens ÷ 60 =
6 tens, or 3600 ÷ 60 = 60. I record 6 in the tens place. There's a
remainder of 7 tens.

b. 3,795 ÷ 62

```
          6                              6  1  R 13
  62 | 3, 7  9  5                 62 | 3, 7  9  5
   -    3  7  2                    -    3  7  2
   _____                    _____
             7                              7  5
                                        -   6  2
                                        _____
                                           1  3
```

I look at 75 and estimate
60 ones ÷ 60 = 1 one, or
60 ÷ 60 = 1. I record 1 in the
ones place. The quotient is 61
with a remainder of 13.

Check:

I check my answer by first multiplying the quotient and the
divisor, and then I add the remainder.

```
        6  1
   ×    6  2
   _____
        1  2  2
   + 3  6  6  0
   _____
     3, 7  8  2
```

```
     3, 7  8  2
   +        1  3
   _____
     3, 7  9  5
```

2. 1,292 balloons were shared equally among 38 students. How many balloons did each student receive?

I use division, 1,292 ÷ 38, to find how many balloons each student receives.

```
           3  4
  38 | 1, 2  9  2
   -    1  1  4
   _____
          1  5  2
        - 1  5  2
        _____
                0
```

Each student received 34 balloons with 0 balloons left over.

Each student received 34 balloons.

EUREKA MATH   Lesson 23: Divide three- and four-digit dividends by two-digit divisors resulting in two- and three-digit quotients, reasoning about the decomposition of successive remainders in each place value.   43

©2015 Great Minds. eureka-math.org
G5-M1-HWH-1.3.0-07.2015

G5-M2-Lesson 24

1. Divide.

   a. $3.5 \div 7 = 0.5$

   > I can use the basic fact of $35 \div 7 = 5$ to help me solve this problem. 3.5 is 35 tenths. 35 tenths $\div 7 = 5$ tenths, or 0.5.

   > Dividing by 70 is the same as dividing by 10 and then dividing by 7.

   b. $3.5 \div 70 = 3.5 \div 10 \div 7$

   $\qquad = 0.35 \div 7$

   $\qquad = 0.05$

   > 35 tenths $\div 10 = 35$ hundredths, or 0.35.

   > 35 hundredths $\div 7 = 5$ hundredths, or 0.05.

   c. $4.84 \div 2 = 2.42$

   > $4.84 = 4$ ones $+ 8$ tenths $+ 4$ hundredths.
   > 4 ones $\div 2 = 2$ ones, or 2.
   > 8 tenths $\div 2 = 4$ tenths, or 0.4.
   > 4 hundredths $\div 2 = 2$ hundredths, or 0.02.
   > The answer is $2 + 0.4 + 0.02 = 2.42$.

   > Dividing by 200 is equal to dividing by 100 and then dividing by 2.
   > Or I can think of it as dividing by 2 and then dividing by 100.

   d. $48.4 \div 200 = 48.4 \div 2 \div 100$

   $\qquad = 24.2 \div 100$

   $\qquad = 0.242$

   > $48 \div 2 = 24$
   > 4 tenths $\div 2 = 2$ tenths or 0.2.
   > So, $48.4 \div 2 = 24.2$.

   > I can visualize a place value chart. When I divide by 100, each digit shifts 2 places to the right.

Lesson 24:   Divide decimal dividends by multiples of 10, reasoning about the placement of the decimal point and making connections to a written method.

©2015 Great Minds. eureka-math.org
G5-M1-HWH-1.3.0-07.2015

EUREKA MATH

2. Use place value reasoning and the first quotient to compute the second quotient. Use place value to explain how you placed the decimal point.

> The dividend, 15.6, is the same in both number sentences.

a. $15.6 \div 60 = 0.26$

> I look at the divisors in both number sentences. They are 60 and 6, respectively. 60 is 10 times as large as 6.

$15.6 \div 6 = 2.6$

> I know the quotient in this problem must be 10 times as large as 0.26, from the problem above. The answer is 26 hundredths × 10 = 26 tenths, or 2.6.

There are 10 times fewer groups, so there has to be 10 times more in each group.

> The dividend, 0.72, is the same in both number sentences.

b. $0.72 \div 4 = 0.18$

> I look at the divisors in both number sentences. They are 4 and 40, respectively. 4 is 10 times smaller than 40.

$0.72 \div 40 = 0.018$

> I know the quotient in this problem must be 10 times smaller than 0.18, from the problem above. The answer is 18 hundredths ÷ 10 = 18 thousandths, or 0.018.

Instead of 4 groups, there are 40 groups. That's 10 times more groups, so there must be 10 times less in each group.

EUREKA MATH

Lesson 24: Divide decimal dividends by multiples of 10, reasoning about the placement of the decimal point and making connections to a written method.

©2015 Great Minds. eureka-math.org
G5-M1-HWH-1.3.0-07.2015

45

G5-M2-Lesson 25

1. Estimate the quotients.

> I look at the divisor, 72, and round it to the nearest ten. $72 \approx 70$

a. $5.68 \div 72$

> I can think of the dividend as 568 hundredths. 560 is close to 568 and a multiple of 70, so I can round 568 hundredths to 560 hundredths.

$\approx 560 \text{ hundredths} \div 70$

$= 560 \text{ hundredths} \div 10 \div 7$

$= 56 \text{ hundredths} \div 7$

> Dividing by 70 is the same as dividing by 10 and then dividing by 7.

$= 8 \text{ hundredths}$

$= 0.08$

> The basic fact $56 \div 7 = 8$ helps me solve this problem.

> I look at the divisor, 41, and round it to the nearest ten. $41 \approx 40$

b. $9.14 \div 41$

> I'll approximate the dividend, 9.14, to be 8. I'll use the basic fact, $8 \div 4 = 2$, to help me solve this problem.

$\approx 8 \div 40$

$= 8 \div 4 \div 10$

> Dividing by 40 is the same as dividing by 4 and then dividing by 10.

$= 2 \div 10$

$= 0.2$

> I can visualize a place value chart. Dividing by 10 moves the digit, 2, one place to the right.

Lesson 25: Use basic facts to approximate decimal quotients with two-digit divisors, reasoning about the placement of the decimal point.

©2015 Great Minds. eureka-math.org
G5-M1-HWH-1.3.0-07.2015

EUREKA MATH

2. Estimate the quotient in (a). Use your estimated quotient to estimate (b) and (c).

$18 \approx 20$

a. $5.29 \div 18$

$\approx 6 \div 20$

$5.29 \approx 6$. I can use the basic fact, $6 \div 2 = 3$, to help me solve this problem.

$= 6 \div 2 \div 10$

$= 3 \div 10$

Dividing by 20 is the same as dividing by 2 and then dividing by 10.

$= 0.3$

Since the digits in this expression are the same as (a), I can use place value understanding to help me solve.

b. $529 \div 18$

I can use the same basic fact, $6 \div 2 = 3$, to help me solve.

$\approx 600 \div 20$

$18 \approx 20$ and $529 \approx 600$

$= 60 \div 2$

$= 30$

$600 \div 20$ is equal to $60 \div 2$ because I divided both the dividend and the divisor by 10.

My quotient makes sense! When I compare (b) to (a), I see that 529 is 100 times greater than 5.29. Therefore, the quotient should be 100 times greater as well. 30 is 100 times greater than 0.3.

c. $52.9 \div 18$

Again, I can use the same basic fact, $6 \div 2 = 3$, to help me solve this problem.

$\approx 60 \div 20$

I'll round 18 to 20 and approximate 52.9 to 60.

$= 6 \div 2$

$= 3$

$60 \div 20$ is equal to $6 \div 2$ because I divided both the dividend and the divisor by 10.

EUREKA MATH™   Lesson 25:   Use basic facts to approximate decimal quotients with two-digit divisors, reasoning about the placement of the decimal point.   47

©2015 Great Minds. eureka-math.org
G5-M1-HWH-1.3.0-07.2015

G5-M2-Lesson 26

1. Divide. Then check your work with multiplication.

   a. $48.07 \div 19 = 2.53$

I can estimate.
40 ones ÷ 20 = 2 ones.
I record a 2 in the ones place.

I can estimate again.
100 tenths ÷ 20 = 5 tenths.
I record a 5 in the tenths place.

I can estimate again.
60 hundredths ÷ 20 = 3 hundredths.
I record a 3 in the hundredths place.

```
        2.
    19 | 4  8.  0  7
     -  3  8
        1  0
```
⟹
```
        2.  5
    19 | 4  8.  0  7
     -  3  8
        1  0  0
     -     9  5
              5
```
⟹
```
        2.  5  3
    19 | 4  8.  0  7
     -  3  8
        1  0  0
     -     9  5
              5  7
           -  5  7
                 0
```

Check: I'll check my answer by multiplying the quotient and the divisor, 2.53 × 19.

```
        2. 5  3
    ×      1  9
    ─────────────
       2  2  7  7
    + 2  5  3  0
    ─────────────
      4  8. 0  7
```

After checking, I get 48.07, which does match the original dividend. So I know I solved it correctly.

Lesson 26:   Divide decimal dividends by two-digit divisors, estimating quotients, reasoning about the placement of the decimal point, and making connections to a written method.

©2015 Great Minds. eureka-math.org
G5-M1-HWH-1.3.0-07.2015

EUREKA MATH™

b. $122.4 \div 51$

```
          2.                                    2. 4
  51 | 1  2  2. 4                       51 | 1  2  2. 4
    -   1  0  2           ⇨               -   1  0  2
    ————————                               ————————
         2  0                                   2  0  4
                                             -  2  0  4
                                             ————————
                                                    0
```

> I can estimate.
> 200 tenths ÷ 50 = 4 tenths.
> I record a 4 in the tenths place.

Check:

> I check my division by multiplying.

```
          5  1
     ×    2. 4
    ————————
          2  0  4
  +  1  0  2  0
    ————————
     1  2  2. 4
```

2.   The weight of 42 identical mini toy soldiers is 109.2 grams. What is the weight of each toy soldier?

```
            2. 6
  42 | 1  0  9. 2
    -     8  4
    ————————
          2  5  2
    -     2  5  2
    ————————
                0
```

> I can use division, 109.2 ÷ 42, to find the weight of each toy soldier.

> 109.2 grams divided by 42 is equal to 2.6 grams with 0 grams remaining.

The weight of each toy soldier is 2. 6 grams.

EUREKA MATH   **Lesson 26:**   Divide decimal dividends by two-digit divisors, estimating quotients,   49
                                    reasoning about the placement of the decimal point, and making
                                    connections to a written method.

©2015 Great Minds. eureka-math.org
G5-M1-HWH-1.3.0-07.2015

G5-M2-Lesson 27

1. Divide. Check your work with multiplication.

    $6.3 \div 18$

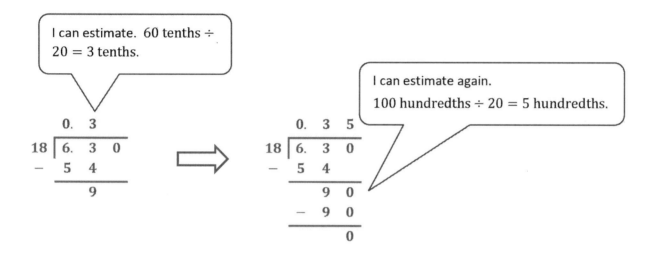

I can estimate. 60 tenths ÷ 20 = 3 tenths.

I can estimate again.
100 hundredths ÷ 20 = 5 hundredths.

I still need to check my work. But since the dividend, 6.3, is less than the divisor, 18, a quotient of less than 1 is reasonable.

Check:

```
      0. 3 5
   ×    1 8
   ─────────
      2 8 0
   + 3 5 0
   ─────────
      6. 3 0
```

After checking, I get 6.30, which does match the original dividend. So I know I divided correctly.

Lesson 27:   Divide decimal dividends by two-digit divisors, estimating quotients, reasoning about the placement of the decimal point, and making connections to a written method.

©2015 Great Minds. eureka-math.org
G5-M1-HWH-1.3.0-07.2015

EUREKA
MATH

2. 43.4 kilograms of raisins was placed into 31 packages of equal weight. What is the weight of one package of raisins?

```
        1.  4
   31 | 4  3.  4
      -  3  1
        ─────────
         1  2  4
      -  1  2  4
        ─────────
               0
```

> I can use division, $43.4 \div 31$, to find the weight of one package.

> 43.4 kilograms divided by 31 is equal to 1.4 kilograms.

The weight of one package of raisins is 1. 4 *kilograms.*

> The quotient is reasonable. Since the dividend, 43.4, is just a little bit more than the divisor, 31, a quotient of 1.4 makes sense.

EUREKA MATH **Lesson 27:** Divide decimal dividends by two-digit divisors, estimating quotients, reasoning about the placement of the decimal point, and making connections to a written method. 51

©2015 Great Minds. eureka-math.org
G5-M1-HWH-1.3.0-07.2015

G5-M2-Lesson 28

1. Juanita is saving for a new television that costs $931. She has already saved half of the money. Juanita earns $19.00 per hour. How many hours must Juanita work to save the rest of the money?

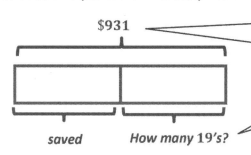

$931

I draw a tape diagram and label the whole as $931. Since she has already saved half, I cut it into 2 equal units.

I have to find how many 19's are in the other half.

saved   How many 19's?

$931 \div 2 = \$465.5$

Since Juanita already saved half of the money, then I'll use $931 divided by 2 to find how much she still needs to save.

$$\begin{array}{r} 4\ 6\ 5.\ 5 \\ 2\overline{\smash{)}9\ 3\ 1.\ 0} \\ -\ 8 \\ \hline 1\ 3 \\ -\ 1\ 2 \\ \hline 1\ 1 \\ -\ 1\ 0 \\ \hline 1\ 0 \\ -\ 1\ 0 \\ \hline 0 \end{array}$$

Juanita already saved $465.50 and will need to save $465.50 more.

Juanita will need to work 24.5 more hours.

$465.5 \div \$19 = 24.5$

Since Juanita makes $19 an hour, then I'll use $465.50 divided by $19 to find how many more hours she will need to work.

$$\begin{array}{r} 2\ 4.\ 5 \\ 19\overline{\smash{)}4\ 6\ 5.\ 5} \\ -\ 3\ 8 \\ \hline 8\ 5 \\ -\ 7\ 6 \\ \hline 9\ 5 \\ -\ 9\ 5 \\ \hline 0 \end{array}$$

I can estimate to help me find the quotient. $465.5 \approx 400$.
40 tens $\div$ 20 = 2 tens.

I estimate again.
80 ones $\div$ 20 = 4 ones.

I estimate a 3rd time.
100 tenths $\div$ 20 = 5 tenths.

Juanita needs to work 24.5 more hours.

Lesson 28:   Solve division word problems involving multi-digit division with group size unknown and the number of groups unknown.

©2015 Great Minds. eureka-math.org
G5-M1-HWH-1.3.0-07.2015

EUREKA MATH

2. Timmy has a collection of 1,008 baseball cards. He hopes to sell the collection in packs of 48 cards and make $178.50 when all the packs are sold. If each pack is priced the same, how much should Timmy charge per pack?

> I need to find out how many packs of baseball cards Timmy has by dividing 1,008 ÷ 48. Then I can find out how much Timmy should charge per pack.

$1,008 \div 48 = 21$

> Timmy will have 21 packs of baseball cards.

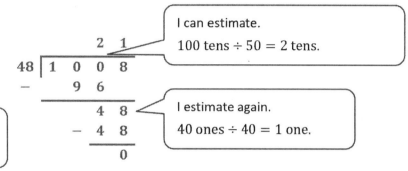

> I can estimate.
> 100 tens ÷ 50 = 2 tens.

> I estimate again.
> 40 ones ÷ 40 = 1 one.

$$\$178.50 \div 21 = \$8.50$$

> The price of each pack of cards needs to be $8.50.

```
        8. 5
21 | 1 7 8. 5
  -  1 6 8
     ———————
       1 0 5
   -   1 0 5
     ———————
           0
```

Timmy should charge $8.50 *per pack.*

EUREKA MATH   **Lesson 28:**   Solve division word problems involving multi-digit division with group size unknown and the number of groups unknown.   53

©2015 Great Minds. eureka-math.org
G5-M1-HWH-1.3.0-07.2015

G5-M2-Lesson 29

1. Alonzo has 2,580.2 kilograms of apples to deliver in equal amounts to 19 stores. Eleven of the stores are in Philadelphia. How many kilograms of apples will be delivered to stores in Philadelphia?

$$2,580.2 \div 19 = 135.8$$

> I can use division to find out how many kilograms of apples are delivered to each store. Each store receives 135.8 kilograms of apples.

```
            1   3   5.  8
    19 | 2   5   8   0.  2
       - 1   9
         ─────
             6   8
           - 5   7
           ─────
               1   1   0
           -       9   5
               ─────
                   1   5   2
               -   1   5   2
                   ─────
                           0
```

$$135.8 \times 11 = 1,493.8$$

> Since I know each store receives 135.8 kilograms of apples, then I use multiplication to find the total kilograms of apples that will be delivered to 11 stores in Philadelphia.

```
            1   3   5.  8
        ×           1   1
        ─────────────────
            1   3   5   8
    +   1   3   5   8   0
    ─────────────────────
        1   4   9   3.  8
```

1493.8 kilograms of apples will be delivered to stores in Philadelphia.

Lesson 29:   Solve division word problems involving multi-digit division with group size unknown and the number of groups unknown.

©2015 Great Minds. eureka-math.org
G5-M1-HWH-1.3.0-07.2015

EUREKA MATH

2. The area of a rectangle is 88.4 m². If the length is 13 m, what is its perimeter?

> In order to find the perimeter, I need to know the width of the rectangle.

area = length × width

width = area ÷ length

$\qquad$ = 88.4 m² ÷ 13 m

$\qquad$ = 6.8 m

```
        6. 8
13 | 8  8.  4
  -  7  8
     ‾‾‾‾‾‾‾
     1  0  4
  -  1  0  4
     ‾‾‾‾‾‾‾
           0
```

> I know the width is equal to the area divided by the length. The width of the rectangle is 6.8 meters.

Perimeter of a rectangle = length + length + width + width

$\qquad$ = 13 m + 13 m + 6.8 m + 6.8 m

$\qquad$ = 26 m + 13.6 m

$\qquad$ = 39.6 m

```
    1 3. 0
    1 3. 0
       6. 8
 +     6. 8
  ‾‾‾‾‾‾‾‾‾
    3 9. 6
```

> I can add up all four sides of the rectangle to find the perimeter.

The perimeter of the rectangle is 39.6 meters.

Homework Helpers

Grade 5
Module 3

G5-M3-Lesson 1

> If I don't have the folded paper strip from class, I can cut a strip of paper about the length of this number line. I can fold it in 2 equal parts. Then, I can use it to label the number line.

1. Use the folded paper strip to mark points 0 and 1 above the number line and $\frac{0}{2}$, $\frac{1}{2}$, and $\frac{2}{2}$ below it.

Draw one vertical line down the middle of each rectangle, creating two parts. Shade the left half of each. Partition with horizontal lines to show the equivalent fractions $\frac{2}{4}$, $\frac{3}{6}$, $\frac{4}{8}$, and $\frac{5}{10}$. Use multiplication to show the change in the units.

1	1	1	1
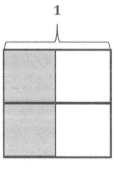	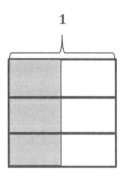	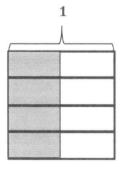	

$$\frac{1}{2} = \frac{1 \times 2}{2 \times 2} = \frac{2}{4}$$

$$\frac{1}{2} = \frac{1 \times 3}{2 \times 3} = \frac{3}{6}$$

$$\frac{1}{2} = \frac{1 \times 4}{2 \times 4} = \frac{4}{8}$$

$$\frac{1}{2} = \frac{1 \times 5}{2 \times 5} = \frac{5}{10}$$

> I started with one whole and divided it into halves by drawing 1 vertical line. I shaded 1 half. Then, I divided the halves into 2 equal parts by drawing a horizontal line. The shading shows me that $\frac{1}{2} = \frac{2}{4}$.

> I did the same with the other models. I divided the halves into smaller units to make sixths, eighths, and tenths.

2. Continue the process, and model 2 equivalent fractions for 4 thirds. Estimate to mark the points on the number line.

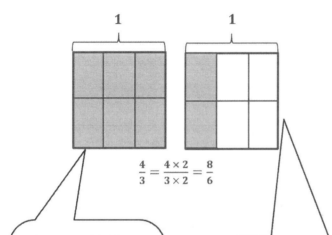

$$\frac{4}{3} = \frac{4 \times 2}{3 \times 2} = \frac{8}{6}$$

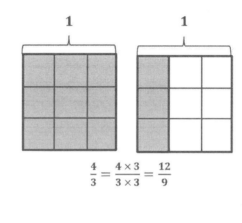

$$\frac{4}{3} = \frac{4 \times 3}{3 \times 3} = \frac{12}{9}$$

> The same thinking works with fractions greater than one. I start by shading 1 and 1 third, which is the same as 4 thirds. To show thirds, I drew vertical lines.

> Then, I partitioned the thirds into a smaller unit, sixths, by drawing horizontal lines.

Lesson 1:   Make equivalent fractions with the number line, the area model, and numbers.

EUREKA
MATH™

G5-M3-Lesson 2

1. Show each expression on a number line. Solve.

   a. $\frac{1}{5} + \frac{1}{5} + \frac{2}{5}$

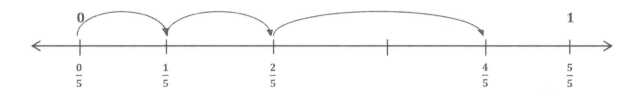

$$\frac{1}{5} + \frac{1}{5} + \frac{2}{5} = \frac{4}{5}$$

> I'm not too concerned about making the jumps on the number line exactly proportional. The number line is just to help me visualize and calculate a solution.

   b. $2 \times \frac{3}{4} + \frac{1}{4}$

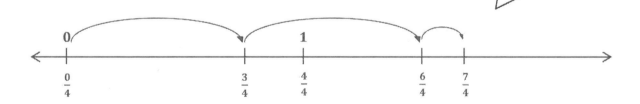

> I can think of this problem in unit form: 2 times 3 fourths plus 1 fourth.

$$2 \times \frac{3}{4} + \frac{1}{4}$$
$$= \frac{6}{4} + \frac{1}{4} = \frac{7}{4}$$

> The answer doesn't have to be simplified. Writing either $\frac{7}{4}$ or $1\frac{3}{4}$ is correct.

©2015 Great Minds. eureka-math.org
G5-M1-HWH-1.3.0-07.2015

2. Express $\frac{6}{5}$ as the sum of two or three equal fractional parts. Rewrite it as a multiplication equation, and then show it on a number line.

$$\frac{3}{5} + \frac{3}{5} = \frac{6}{5} \qquad 2 \times \frac{3}{5} = \frac{6}{5}$$

Since the directions asked for a sum, I know I have to show an addition equation.

$2 \times \frac{3}{5}$ is equivalent to $\frac{3}{5} + \frac{3}{5}$.

Another correct solution is $\frac{2}{5} + \frac{2}{5} + \frac{2}{5} = 3 \times \frac{2}{5}$.

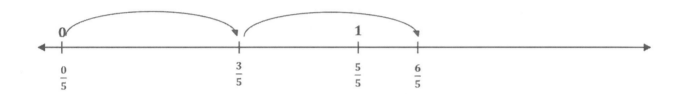

3. Express $\frac{7}{3}$ as the sum of a whole number and a fraction. Show on a number line.

$$\frac{7}{3} = \frac{6}{3} + \frac{1}{3}$$

$$= 2 + \frac{1}{3}$$

$$= 2\frac{1}{3}$$

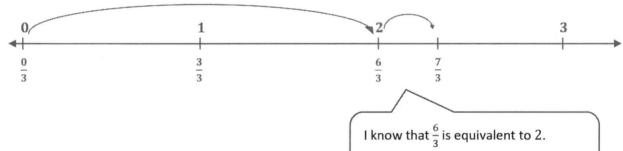

I know that $\frac{6}{3}$ is equivalent to 2.

$\frac{6}{3} = \frac{3}{3} + \frac{3}{3}$. This is the same as $1 + 1$.

EUREKA MATH™

 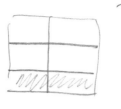

G5-M3-Lesson 3

Draw a rectangular fraction model to find the sum. Simplify your answer, if possible.

a. $\frac{1}{2} + \frac{1}{3} = \frac{5}{6}$

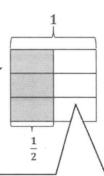 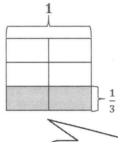

First, I make 2 identical wholes. I shade $\frac{1}{2}$ vertically. In the other whole I can show $\frac{1}{3}$ by drawing 2 horizontal lines.

I need to make like units in order to add. I partition the halves into sixths by drawing 2 horizontal lines.

$\frac{1}{2} = \frac{3}{6}$

I divide the thirds into sixths by drawing a vertical line. In both models, I have like units: sixths.

$\frac{1}{3} = \frac{2}{6}$

$$\frac{1}{2} + \frac{1}{3} = \frac{3}{6} + \frac{2}{6} = \frac{5}{6}$$

b. $\frac{2}{7} + \frac{2}{3} = \frac{20}{21}$

These addends are non-unit fractions because both have numerators greater than one.

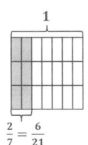 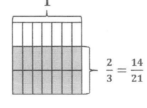

$\frac{2}{3} = \frac{14}{21}$

$\frac{2}{7} = \frac{6}{21}$

$$\frac{2}{7} + \frac{2}{3} = \frac{6}{21} + \frac{14}{21} = \frac{20}{21}$$

G5-M3-Lesson 4

For the following problem, draw a picture using the rectangular fraction model, and write the answer. If possible, write your answer as a mixed number.

$\frac{1}{2} + \frac{3}{4}$

I need to make like units before adding.

My model shows me that $\frac{3}{4} = \frac{6}{8}$.

By partitioning 1 half into 4 equal parts, I can see that $\frac{1}{2} = \frac{4}{8}$.

1   1

$\frac{1}{2}$

$\frac{3}{4}$

My solution of $1\frac{2}{8}$ makes sense. When I look at the fraction models and think about adding them together, I can see that they would make 1 whole and 2 eighths when combined.

$$\frac{1}{2} + \frac{3}{4} = \frac{4}{8} + \frac{6}{8} = \frac{10}{8} = 1\frac{2}{8}$$

I don't need to express my solution in simplest form, but if wanted to, I could show that $1\frac{2}{8} = 1\frac{1}{4}$.

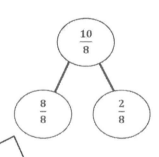

I can use a number bond to rename $\frac{10}{8}$ as a mixed number. This part-part-whole model shows that 10 eighths is composed of 8 eighths and 2 eighths.

©2015 Great Minds. eureka-math.org
G5-M1-HWH-1.3.0-07.2015

G5-M3-Lesson 5

1. Find the difference. Use a rectangular fraction model to find a common unit. Simplify your answer, if possible.

$$\frac{2}{3} - \frac{1}{4} = \frac{5}{12}$$

> In order to subtract fourths from thirds, I need to find like units.

> I draw 3 horizontal lines to partition my model into fourths and shade 1 of them to show the fraction $\frac{1}{4}$.

> I draw 2 vertical lines to partition my model into thirds and shade 2 of them to show the fraction $\frac{2}{3}$.

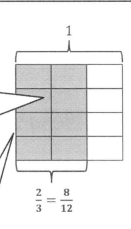

$$\frac{1}{4} = \frac{3}{12}$$

$$\frac{2}{3} = \frac{8}{12}$$

> In order to make like units, or common denominators, I draw 3 horizontal lines to partition the model into 12 equal parts. Now, I can see that $\frac{2}{3} = \frac{8}{12}$.

> I still can't subtract. Fourths and twelfths are different units. But, I can draw 2 vertical lines to partition the model into 12 equal parts. Now, I have equal units and can see that $\frac{1}{4} = \frac{3}{12}$.

$$\frac{2}{3} - \frac{1}{4} = \frac{8}{12} - \frac{3}{12} = \frac{5}{12}$$

> Once I have like units, the subtraction is simple. I know that 8 minus 3 is equal to 5, so I can think of this in unit form very simply.
>
> 8 twelfths − 3 twelfths = 5 twelfths

2. Lisbeth needs $\frac{1}{3}$ of a tablespoon of spice for a baking recipe. She has $\frac{5}{6}$ of a tablespoon in her pantry. How much spice will Lisbeth have after baking?

> I'll need to subtract $\frac{1}{3}$ from $\frac{5}{6}$ to find out how much remains.

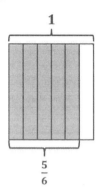

$$\frac{5}{6}$$

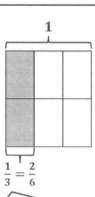

$$\frac{1}{3} = \frac{2}{6}$$

> This was interesting! After drawing the $\frac{5}{6}$ that Lisbeth has in her pantry, I realized that thirds and sixths are related units. In this problem, I could leave $\frac{5}{6}$ as is and only rename the thirds as sixths to find a common unit.

$$\frac{5}{6} - \frac{1}{3} = \frac{5}{6} - \frac{2}{6} = \frac{3}{6}$$

Lisbeth will have $\frac{3}{6}$ of a tablespoon of spice after baking.

> I could also express $\frac{3}{6}$ as $\frac{1}{2}$ because they are equivalent fractions, but I don't have to.

> In order to finish the problem, I must make a statement to answer the question.

Lesson 5:   Subtract fractions with unlike units using the strategy of creating equivalent fractions.

EUREKA MATH™

G5-M3-Lesson 6

For the following problems, draw a picture using the rectangular fraction model, and write the answer. Simplify your answer, if possible.

a. $\frac{4}{3} - \frac{1}{2} = \frac{5}{6}$

> In order to subtract halves from thirds, I'll need to find a common unit. I can rename them both as a number of sixths.

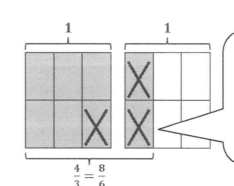

> I can cross out the $\frac{3}{6}$ that I'm subtracting to see the $\frac{5}{6}$ that represents the difference.

$$\frac{4}{3} - \frac{1}{2} = \frac{8}{6} - \frac{3}{6} = \frac{5}{6}$$

$$\frac{4}{3} = \frac{3}{3} + \frac{1}{3} = 1 + \frac{1}{3} \quad \text{and} \quad \frac{8}{6} = \frac{6}{6} + \frac{2}{6} = 1 + \frac{2}{6}$$

> In order to subtract fourths from thirds, I'll need to find a common unit. I can rename them both as a number of twelfths.

b. $1\frac{2}{3} - \frac{3}{4} = \frac{11}{12}$

> This time, I'll subtract $\frac{3}{4}$ (or $\frac{9}{12}$) all at once from the 1 (or the $\frac{12}{12}$).

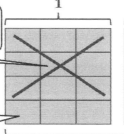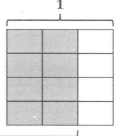

> Then, in order to find the difference, I can add these $\frac{3}{12}$ to the $\frac{8}{12}$ in the fraction model to the right.

$$1\frac{2}{3} = \frac{5}{3} = \frac{20}{12}$$

> I can use the fraction model and this number bond to help me see that $1\frac{2}{3}$ is composed of $\frac{12}{12}$ and $\frac{8}{12}$.

$$1\frac{2}{3} - \frac{3}{4} = \frac{3}{12} + \frac{8}{12} = \frac{11}{12}$$

©2015 Great Minds. eureka-math.org
G5-M1-HWH-1.3.0-07.2015

G5-M3-Lesson 7

RDW means "Read, Draw, Write." I **read** the problem several times. I **draw** something each time I read. I remember to **write** the answer to the question.

Solve the word problems using the RDW strategy.

1. Rosie has a collection of comic books. She gave $\frac{1}{2}$ of them to her brother. Rosie gave $\frac{1}{6}$ of them to her friend, and she kept the rest. How much of the collection did Rosie keep for herself?

If I subtract $\frac{1}{2}$ and $\frac{1}{6}$ from 1, I can find how much of the collection Rosie kept for herself.

I can draw a tape diagram to model this problem.

$1 - \frac{1}{2} - \frac{1}{6}$

Rosie's Collection

$\frac{1}{2}$	$\frac{1}{6}$	?

brother   friend   kept

$= \frac{1}{2} - \frac{1}{6}$

$= \frac{3}{6} - \frac{1}{6}$

$= \frac{2}{6}$

I've been doing so much of this that now I can rename some fractions in my head. I know that $\frac{1}{2} = \frac{3}{6}$.

Rosie kept $\frac{2}{6}$ or $\frac{1}{3}$ of the collection for herself.

When I think of this another way, I know that my solution makes sense. I can think $\frac{1}{2} + \frac{1}{6} +$ "how much more" is equal to 1?

$$\frac{1}{2} + \frac{1}{6} + ? = 1 \quad \rightarrow \quad \frac{3}{6} + \frac{1}{6} + \frac{2}{6} = \frac{6}{6} = 1$$

©2015 Great Minds. eureka-math.org
G5-M1-HWH-1.3.0-07.2015

2. Ken ran for $\frac{1}{4}$ mile. Peggy ran $\frac{1}{3}$ mile farther than Ken. How far did they run altogether?

Ken | $\frac{1}{4}$ mi |

Peggy | | $\frac{1}{3}$ mi | ?

> To find the distance they ran altogether, I'll add Ken's distance ($\frac{1}{4}$ mile) to Peggy's distance ($\frac{1}{4}$ mile $+ \frac{1}{3}$ mile).

> My tape diagram shows that Peggy ran the same distance as Ken plus $\frac{1}{3}$ mile farther.

$$\frac{1}{4} + \frac{1}{4} + \frac{1}{3}$$
$$= \frac{1}{2} + \frac{1}{3}$$
$$= \frac{3}{6} + \frac{2}{6}$$
$$= \frac{5}{6}$$

> I could rename all of these as a number of twelfths, but I know that $\frac{1}{4} + \frac{1}{4} = \frac{2}{4}$, which is equal to $\frac{1}{2}$.

> Now, I can rename these halves and thirds as sixths. I can do this renaming mentally!

Ken and Peggy ran $\frac{5}{6}$ mile altogether.

G5-M3-Lesson 8

1. Add or subtract. Draw a number line to model your solution.

    a. $9\frac{1}{3} + 6 = 15\frac{1}{3}$

    $9\frac{1}{3}$ is the same as $9 + \frac{1}{3}$. I can add the whole numbers, $9 + 6 = 15$, and then add the fraction, $15 + \frac{1}{3} = 15\frac{1}{3}$.

    I can model this addition using a number line. I'll start at 0 and add 9.

    I add 6 to get to 15.

    Then, I add $\frac{1}{3}$ to get to $15\frac{1}{3}$.

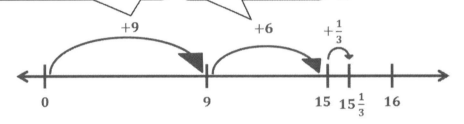

    b. $18 - 13\frac{3}{4} = 4\frac{1}{4}$

    $13\frac{3}{4}$ is the same as $13 + \frac{3}{4}$. I can subtract the whole numbers first, $18 - 13 = 5$. Then, I can subtract the fraction, $5 - \frac{3}{4} = 4\frac{1}{4}$.

    I start at 18 and subtract 13 to get 5. Then, I subtract $\frac{3}{4}$ to get $4\frac{1}{4}$.

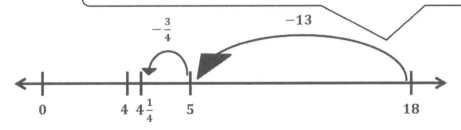

Lesson 8:   Add fractions to and subtract fractions from whole numbers using
                equivalence and the number line as strategies.

©2015 Great Minds. eureka-math.org
G5-M1-HWH-1.3.0-07.2015

**EUREKA
MATH**

2. The total length of two strings is 15 meters. If one string is $8\frac{3}{5}$ meters long, what is the length of the other string?

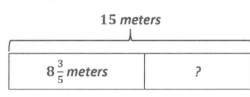

15 *meters*

| $8\frac{3}{5}$ *meters* | ? |

I can use subtraction, $15 - 8\frac{3}{5}$, to find the length of the other string.

My tape diagram models this word problem. I need to find the length of the missing part.

$15 - 8\frac{3}{5} = 6\frac{2}{5}$

I can draw a number line to solve. I'll start at 15 and subtract 8 to get 7. Then, I'll subtract $\frac{3}{5}$ to get $6\frac{2}{5}$.

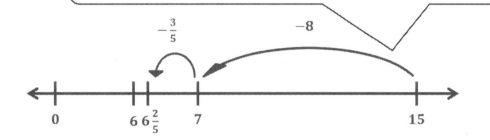

$-\frac{3}{5}$ -8

0      $6\ 6\frac{2}{5}\ 7$ 15

The length of the other string is $6\frac{2}{5}$ meters.

Below is an alternative method to solve this problem.

Now, I can subtract the whole numbers and subtract the fractions.
$$14 - 8 = 6$$
$$\frac{5}{5} - \frac{3}{5} = \frac{2}{5}$$
The difference is $6\frac{2}{5}$.

I can express 15 as a mixed number, $14\frac{5}{5}$.

$15 - 8\frac{3}{5}$

14        $\frac{5}{5}$ ⟶ $14\frac{5}{5} - 8\frac{3}{5} = 6\frac{2}{5}$

EUREKA MATH   Lesson 8: Add fractions to and subtract fractions from whole numbers using equivalence and the number line as strategies.   13

©2015 Great Minds. eureka-math.org
G5-M1-HWH-1.3.0-07.2015

G5-M3-Lesson 9

1. First, make like units, and then add.

The denominators here are thirds and fifths. I can skip count to find a like unit.

3: 3, 6, 9, 12, **15**, 18, …

5: 5, 10, **15**, 20, …

15 is a multiple of both 3 and 5, so I can make like units of fifteenths.

I can multiply both the numerator and the denominator by 5 to rename $\frac{1}{3}$ as a number of fifteenths.

$$\frac{1 \times 5}{3 \times 5} = \frac{5}{15}$$

I can multiply both the numerator and the denominator by 3 to rename $\frac{2}{5}$ as a number of fifteenths.

$$\frac{2 \times 3}{5 \times 3} = \frac{6}{15}$$

a. $\frac{1}{3} + \frac{2}{5} = \left(\frac{1 \times 5}{3 \times 5}\right) + \left(\frac{2 \times 3}{5 \times 3}\right)$

$$= \frac{5}{15} + \frac{6}{15}$$

$$= \frac{11}{15}$$

5 fifteenths + 6 fifteenths = 11 fifteenths

EUREKA MATH™

The denominators here are sixths and eighths. I can skip count to find a like unit.

6: 6, 12, 18, **24**, 30, …

8: 8, 16, **24**, 32, …

24 is a multiple of both 6 and 8, so I can make like units of twenty-fourths.

I can multiply both the numerator and the denominator by 4 to rename $\frac{5}{6}$ as a number of twenty-fourths.

$$\frac{5 \times 4}{6 \times 4} = \frac{20}{24}$$

b. $\frac{5}{6} + \frac{3}{8} = \left(\frac{5 \times 4}{6 \times 4}\right) + \left(\frac{3 \times 3}{8 \times 3}\right)$

I can multiply both the numerator and the denominator by 3 to rename $\frac{3}{8}$ as a number of twenty-fourths.

$$\frac{3 \times 3}{8 \times 3} = \frac{9}{24}$$

$$= \frac{20}{24} + \frac{9}{24}$$

$$= \frac{29}{24}$$

$$= \frac{24}{24} + \frac{5}{24}$$

$$= 1\frac{5}{24}$$

$\frac{29}{24}$ is the same as $\frac{24}{24}$ plus $\frac{5}{24}$, or $1\frac{5}{24}$.

The like unit for ninths and halves is eighteenths.

c. $\frac{4}{9} + 1\frac{1}{2} = \left(\frac{4 \times 2}{9 \times 2}\right) + \left(\frac{1 \times 9}{2 \times 9}\right) + 1$

I can add the 1 after adding the fractions.

$$= \frac{8}{18} + \frac{9}{18} + 1$$

$$= \frac{17}{18} + 1$$

$$= 1\frac{17}{18}$$

$\frac{17}{18}$ plus 1 is the same as the mixed number $1\frac{17}{18}$.

©2015 Great Minds. eureka-math.org
G5-M1-HWH-1.3.0-07.2015

2. On Tuesday, Karol spent $\frac{3}{4}$ of one hour on reading homework and $\frac{1}{3}$ of one hour on math homework. How much time did Karol spend doing her reading and math homework on Tuesday?

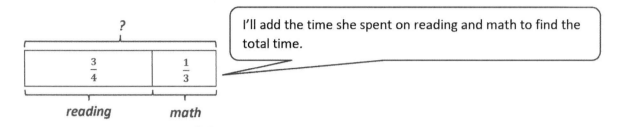

I'll add the time she spent on reading and math to find the total time.

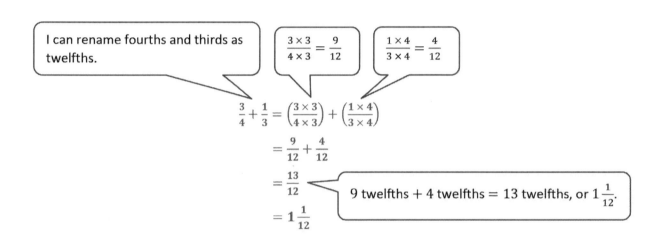

I can rename fourths and thirds as twelfths.

$$\frac{3 \times 3}{4 \times 3} = \frac{9}{12}$$

$$\frac{1 \times 4}{3 \times 4} = \frac{4}{12}$$

$$\frac{3}{4} + \frac{1}{3} = \left(\frac{3 \times 3}{4 \times 3}\right) + \left(\frac{1 \times 4}{3 \times 4}\right)$$

$$= \frac{9}{12} + \frac{4}{12}$$

$$= \frac{13}{12}$$

9 twelfths + 4 twelfths = 13 twelfths, or $1\frac{1}{12}$.

$$= 1\frac{1}{12}$$

Karol spent $1\frac{1}{12}$ hours doing her reading and math homework.

EUREKA
MATH™

G5-M3-Lesson 10

I'll add the whole numbers first and then add the fractions. $4 + 2 = 6$

1. Add.

a. $4\frac{2}{5} + 2\frac{1}{3} = 6 + \frac{2}{5} + \frac{1}{3}$

$= 6 + \left(\frac{2 \times 3}{5 \times 3}\right) + \left(\frac{1 \times 5}{3 \times 5}\right)$ ← I need to make like units before adding.

$= 6 + \frac{6}{15} + \frac{5}{15}$

$= 6 + \frac{11}{15}$

$= 6\frac{11}{15}$

I can rename these fractions as a number of fifteenths.

$\frac{2}{5} = \frac{6}{15}$, and $\frac{1}{3} = \frac{5}{15}$.

The sum is $6\frac{11}{15}$.

I'll add the whole numbers together. $5 + 10 = 15$.

b. $5\frac{2}{7} + 10\frac{3}{4} = 15 + \frac{2}{7} + \frac{3}{4}$

$= 15 + \left(\frac{2 \times 4}{7 \times 4}\right) + \left(\frac{3 \times 7}{4 \times 7}\right)$

$= 15 + \frac{8}{28} + \frac{21}{28}$

$= 15 + \frac{29}{28}$

$= 15 + \frac{28}{28} + \frac{1}{28}$

$= 16\frac{1}{28}$

When I look at $\frac{2}{7}$ and $\frac{3}{4}$, I decide to use 28 as the common unit, which will be the new denominator.

$\frac{2}{7} = \frac{8}{28}$

$\frac{3}{4} = \frac{21}{28}$

I know $\frac{29}{28}$ is more than 1. So, I'll rewrite $\frac{29}{28}$ as $\frac{28}{28} + \frac{1}{28}$.

The sum is $16\frac{1}{28}$.

2. Jillian bought some ribbon. She used $3\frac{3}{4}$ meters for an art project and had $5\frac{1}{10}$ meters left. What was the original length of the ribbon?

> I can add to find the original length of the ribbon.

> I draw a tape diagram and label the used ribbon $3\frac{3}{4}$ meters and the leftover ribbon $5\frac{1}{10}$ meters.

> I label the whole ribbon with a question mark because that's what I'm trying to find.

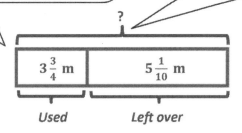

?

| $3\frac{3}{4}$ m | $5\frac{1}{10}$ m |

      Used   *Left over*

> I'll add 3 plus 5 to get 8.

> I need to rename fourths and tenths as a common unit before adding. When I skip-count, I know that 20 is a multiple of both 4 and 10.

$$3\frac{3}{4} + 5\frac{1}{10} = 8 + \frac{3}{4} + \frac{1}{10}$$

$$= 8 + \left(\frac{3 \times 5}{4 \times 5}\right) + \left(\frac{1 \times 2}{10 \times 2}\right)$$

$$= 8 + \frac{15}{20} + \frac{2}{20}$$

> $\frac{3}{4} = \frac{15}{20}$, and $\frac{1}{10} = \frac{2}{20}$.

$$= 8\frac{17}{20}$$

The original length of the ribbon was $8\frac{17}{20}$ meters.

Lesson 10:   Add fractions with sums greater than 2.

EUREKA MATH

G5-M3-Lesson 11

1. Generate equivalent fractions to get like units and then, subtract.

a. $\frac{3}{4} - \frac{1}{3}$

$= \frac{9}{12} - \frac{4}{12}$

$= \frac{5}{12}$

> I can rename fourths and thirds as twelfths in order to subtract.
> $\frac{3}{4} = \frac{9}{12}$ and $\frac{1}{3} = \frac{4}{12}$.

> 9 twelfths − 4 twelfths = 5 twelfths

b. $3\frac{4}{5} - 2\frac{1}{2}$

> I can rename halves and fifths as tenths to subtract. I can solve this problem in several different ways.

Method 1:

> I can rewrite the mixed numbers with a common denominator of 10.
> $3\frac{4}{5} = 3\frac{8}{10}$, and $2\frac{1}{2} = 2\frac{5}{10}$.

$3\frac{4}{5} - 2\frac{1}{2}$

$= 3\frac{8}{10} - 2\frac{5}{10}$

$= 1\frac{3}{10}$

> Now, I can subtract the whole numbers and then the fractions.
> $3 - 2 = 1$, and $\frac{8}{10} - \frac{5}{10} = \frac{3}{10}$.

> The answer is $1 + \frac{3}{10}$, or $1\frac{3}{10}$.

Method 2:

> I can subtract the whole numbers first. $3 - 2 = 1$

$3\frac{4}{5} - 2\frac{1}{2}$

$= 1\frac{4}{5} - \frac{1}{2}$

$= 1\frac{8}{10} - \frac{5}{10}$

$= 1\frac{3}{10}$

> Then, I can rename the fractions using a common denominator of 10.
> $1\frac{4}{5} = 1\frac{8}{10}$, and $\frac{1}{2} = \frac{5}{10}$.

> I can subtract the fractions.
> $\frac{8}{10} - \frac{5}{10} = \frac{3}{10}$

> The difference is $1\frac{3}{10}$.

Method 3:

I can also decompose $3\frac{4}{5}$ into two parts using a number bond.

$$3\frac{4}{5} - 2\frac{1}{2}$$

Now, I can easily subtract $2\frac{1}{2}$ from 3.

$$3 - 2\frac{1}{2} = \frac{1}{2}$$

After subtracting $2\frac{1}{2}$, I can add the remaining fractions, $\frac{1}{2}$ and $\frac{4}{5}$.

$$= \frac{1}{2} + \frac{4}{5}$$

$$= \frac{5}{10} + \frac{8}{10}$$

$$= \frac{13}{10}$$

$$= 1\frac{3}{10}$$

I can rename these fractions as tenths in order to add.

$$\frac{1}{2} = \frac{5}{10}, \text{ and } \frac{4}{5} = \frac{8}{10}.$$

The sum of 5 tenths and 8 tenths is 13 tenths. $\frac{13}{10} = \frac{10}{10} + \frac{3}{10} = 1\frac{3}{10}$

Method 4:

I could also rename the mixed numbers as fractions greater than one.

$$3\frac{4}{5} = \frac{15}{5} + \frac{4}{5} = \frac{19}{5}, \text{ and}$$

$$2\frac{1}{2} = \frac{4}{2} + \frac{1}{2} = \frac{5}{2}.$$

$$3\frac{4}{5} - 2\frac{1}{2}$$

$$= \frac{19}{5} - \frac{5}{2}$$

$$= \frac{38}{10} - \frac{25}{10}$$

$$= \frac{13}{10}$$

$$= 1\frac{3}{10}$$

Then, I can rename the fractions greater than one with the common denominator of 10.

$$\frac{19}{5} = \frac{38}{10}, \text{ and } \frac{5}{2} = \frac{25}{10}.$$

38 tenths minus 25 tenths is 13 tenths. $\frac{13}{10} = \frac{10}{10} + \frac{3}{10} = 1\frac{3}{10}.$

Lesson 11:   Subtract fractions making like units numerically.   EUREKA MATH

©2015 Great Minds. eureka-math.org
G5-M1-HWH-1.3.0-07.2015

G5-M3-Lesson 12

1. Subtract.

   ⟨ I can subtract these mixed numbers using a variety of strategies. ⟩

   a. $3\frac{1}{4} - 2\frac{1}{3}$ ⟨ I can rename these fractions as twelfths in order to subtract. ⟩

Method 1:

⟨ I can subtract the whole numbers. $3 - 2 = 1$ ⟩

$$3\frac{1}{4} - 2\frac{1}{3}$$

$$= 1\frac{1}{4} - \frac{1}{3}$$

⟨ I can rename the fractions with a common unit of 12. $1\frac{1}{4} = 1\frac{3}{12}$, and $\frac{1}{3} = \frac{4}{12}$. ⟩

$$= 1\frac{3}{12} - \frac{4}{12}$$

$$= \frac{15}{12} - \frac{4}{12}$$

⟨ I can't subtract the fraction $\frac{4}{12}$ from $\frac{3}{12}$, so I can rename $1\frac{3}{12}$ as a fraction greater than one, $\frac{15}{12}$. ⟩

$$= \frac{11}{12}$$

⟨ 15 twelfths − 4 twelfths = 11 twelfths ⟩

Method 2:

⟨ Or, I could decompose $3\frac{1}{4}$ into two parts with a number bond. ⟩

$$3\frac{1}{4} - 2\frac{1}{3}$$

        3        $\frac{1}{4}$

⟨ Now, I can easily subtract $2\frac{1}{3}$ from 3. $3 - 2\frac{1}{3} = \frac{2}{3}$ ⟩

$$= \frac{2}{3} + \frac{1}{4}$$

⟨ After subtracting $2\frac{1}{3}$, I can add the remaining fractions, $\frac{2}{3}$ and $\frac{1}{4}$. ⟩

$$= \frac{8}{12} + \frac{3}{12}$$

⟨ I can rename these fractions as twelfths in order to add. $\frac{2}{3} = \frac{8}{12}$, and $\frac{1}{4} = \frac{3}{12}$. ⟩

$$= \frac{11}{12}$$

⟨ The sum of 8 twelfths and 3 twelfths is 11 twelfths. ⟩

Or, I could rename both mixed numbers as fractions greater than one.

$3\frac{1}{4} = \frac{13}{4}$, and $2\frac{1}{3} = \frac{7}{3}$.

Method 3:

$3\frac{1}{4} - 2\frac{1}{3}$

And, I can rename the fractions greater than one using the common unit twelfths.

$\frac{13}{4} = \frac{39}{12}$, and $\frac{7}{3} = \frac{28}{12}$.

$= \frac{13}{4} - \frac{7}{3}$

$= \frac{39}{12} - \frac{28}{12}$

$= \frac{11}{12}$

39 twelfths minus 28 twelfths is equal to 11 twelfths.

b. $19\frac{1}{3} - 4\frac{6}{7}$

Method 1:

$19\frac{1}{3} - 4\frac{6}{7}$

I need to make a common unit before subtracting. I can rename these fractions using a denominator of 21.

I can subtract the whole numbers, $19 - 4 = 15$

$= 15\frac{1}{3} - \frac{6}{7}$

$= 15\frac{7}{21} - \frac{18}{21}$

$15\frac{7}{21} = 14 + 1 + \frac{7}{21}$

$= 14 + \frac{21}{21} + \frac{7}{21}$

$= 14 + \frac{28}{21}$

$= 14\frac{28}{21}$

$= 14\frac{28}{21} - \frac{18}{21}$

$= 14\frac{10}{21}$

I can't subtract $\frac{18}{21}$ from $\frac{7}{21}$, so I rename $15\frac{7}{21}$ as $14\frac{28}{21}$.

Method 2:

I want to subtract $4\frac{6}{7}$ from 5, so I can decompose $19\frac{1}{3}$ into two parts with this number bond.

$5 - 4\frac{6}{7} = \frac{1}{7}$

Now, I need to combine $\frac{1}{7}$ with the remaining part, $14\frac{1}{3}$.

$19\frac{1}{3} - 4\frac{6}{7} = \frac{1}{7} + 14\frac{1}{3}$

$= \frac{3}{21} + 14\frac{7}{21}$

$= 14\frac{10}{21}$

In order to add, I'll rename these fractions using a common denominator of 21.

$14\frac{1}{3}$ 5

Lesson 12:   Subtract fractions greater than or equal to 1.   **EUREKA MATH**

G5-M3-Lesson 13

1. Are the following expressions greater than or less than 1? Circle the correct answer.

   a. $\frac{1}{2} + \frac{3}{5}$ (greater than 1)   less than 1

   > I know that $\frac{1}{2}$ plus $\frac{1}{2}$ is exactly 1. I also know that $\frac{3}{5}$ is greater than $\frac{1}{2}$. Therefore, $\frac{1}{2}$ plus a number greater than $\frac{1}{2}$ must be greater than 1.

   b. $3\frac{1}{4} - 2\frac{2}{3}$ greater than 1   (less than 1)

   > I know that $3 - 2 = 1$, so this expression is the same as $1\frac{1}{4} - \frac{2}{3}$. I also know that $\frac{2}{3}$ is greater than $\frac{1}{4}$. Therefore, if I were to subtract $\frac{2}{3}$ from $1\frac{1}{4}$, the difference would be less than 1.

2. Are the following expressions greater than or less than $\frac{1}{2}$? Circle the correct answer.

   $\frac{1}{3} + \frac{1}{4}$ (greater than $\frac{1}{2}$)   less than $\frac{1}{2}$

   > I know that $\frac{1}{4}$ plus $\frac{1}{4}$ is exactly $\frac{1}{2}$. I also know that $\frac{1}{3}$ is greater than $\frac{1}{4}$. Therefore, $\frac{1}{4}$ plus a number greater than $\frac{1}{4}$ must be greater than $\frac{1}{2}$.

3. Use $>$, $<$, or $=$ to make the following statement true.

   $6\frac{3}{4} \underline{\quad > \quad} 2\frac{4}{5} + 3\frac{1}{3}$

   > I know that 3 plus $3\frac{1}{3}$ is equal to $6\frac{1}{3}$, which is less than $6\frac{3}{4}$.
   >
   > Therefore, a number less than 3 plus $3\frac{1}{3}$ is definitely going to be less than $6\frac{3}{4}$.

EUREKA MATH   **Lesson 13:**   Use fraction benchmark numbers to assess reasonableness of addition and subtraction equations.   23

©2015 Great Minds. eureka-math.org
G5-M1-HWH-1.3.0-07.2015

G5-M3-Lesson 14

1. Rearrange the terms so that you can add or subtract mentally, and then solve.

   a. $2\frac{1}{3} - \frac{3}{5} + \frac{2}{3} = \left(2\frac{1}{3} + \frac{2}{3}\right) - \frac{3}{5}$

   > The associative property allows me to rearrange these terms so that I can add the like units first.

   $= 3 - \frac{3}{5}$

   $= 2\frac{2}{5}$

   > Wow! This is actually a really basic problem now!

   b. $8\frac{3}{4} - 2\frac{2}{5} - 1\frac{1}{5} - \frac{3}{4} = \left(8\frac{3}{4} - \frac{3}{4}\right) - \left(2\frac{2}{5} + 1\frac{1}{5}\right)$

   > This expression has fourths and fifths. I can use the associative property to rearrange the like units together.

   $= 8 - 3\frac{3}{5}$

   $= 5 - \frac{3}{5}$

   $= 4\frac{2}{5}$

   > Subtracting $2\frac{2}{5}$ and then subtracting $1\frac{1}{5}$ is the same as subtracting $3\frac{3}{5}$ all at once.

2. Fill in the blank to make the statement true.

   > In order to add fourths and thirds, I need a common unit. I can rename both fractions as twelfths.

   a. $3\frac{1}{4} + 2\frac{2}{3} + 3\frac{1}{12} = 9$

   $3\frac{3}{12} + 2\frac{8}{12} + \underline{} = 9$

   $5\frac{11}{12} + \underline{} = 9$

   $5\frac{11}{12} + 3\frac{1}{12} = 9$

   > I could solve this by subtracting $5\frac{11}{12}$ from 9, but I'm going to count on from $5\frac{11}{12}$ instead.

   > $5\frac{11}{12}$ needs $\frac{1}{12}$ more to make 6. And then, 6 needs 3 more to make 9. So, $5\frac{11}{12} + 3\frac{1}{12} = 9$.

   $$5\frac{11}{12} \xrightarrow{+\frac{1}{12}} 6 \xrightarrow{+3} 9$$

EUREKA MATH

When I look at this equation, I think, "There is *some number* that, when I subtract $2\frac{1}{2}$ and 15 from it, there is still $17\frac{1}{4}$ remaining." This helps me to visualize a tape diagram like this:

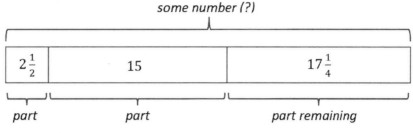

some number (?)

| $2\frac{1}{2}$ | 15 | $17\frac{1}{4}$ |

part   part   part remaining

b. $34\frac{3}{4} - 2\frac{1}{2} - 15 = 17\frac{1}{4}$

Therefore, if I add together these 3 parts, I can find out what that missing number is.

$$2\frac{1}{2} + 15 + 17\frac{1}{4}$$
$$= 34 + \left(\frac{1}{2} + \frac{1}{4}\right)$$
$$= 34\frac{3}{4}$$

I can add the whole numbers and then add the fractions.

I can rename $\frac{1}{2}$ as $\frac{2}{4}$ in my head in order to add like units.

G5-M3-Lesson 15

1. Nikki bought 10 meters of cloth. She used $2\frac{1}{4}$ meters for a dress and $1\frac{3}{5}$ meters for a shirt. How much cloth did she have left?

> There are different ways to solve this problem. I could subtract the length of the dress and the shirt from the total length of the cloth.

> I'll draw a tape diagram and label the whole as 10 m and the parts as $2\frac{1}{4}$ m and $1\frac{3}{5}$ m.

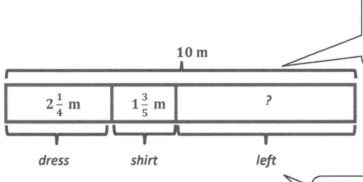

10 m

| $2\frac{1}{4}$ m | $1\frac{3}{5}$ m | ? |

dress   shirt   left

> I'll label the part that's left with a question mark because that's what I'm trying to find.

> I can subtract the whole numbers first.
>
> $10 - 2 - 1 = 7$

$$10 - 2\frac{1}{4} - 1\frac{3}{5}$$

> I can rename these fractions as twentieths in order to subtract.
>
> $\frac{1}{4} = \frac{5}{20}$, and $\frac{3}{5} = \frac{12}{20}$.

$$= 7 - \frac{1}{4} - \frac{3}{5}$$

$$= 7 - \frac{5}{20} - \frac{12}{20}$$

$$= 6\frac{20}{20} - \frac{5}{20} - \frac{12}{20}$$

> I need to rename 7 as $6\frac{20}{20}$ so I can subtract.

$$= 6\frac{3}{20}$$

She had $6\frac{3}{20}$ meters of cloth left.

        Lesson 15:   Solve multi-step word problems; assess reasonableness of solutions using benchmark numbers.

©2015 Great Minds. eureka-math.org
G5-M1-HWH-1.3.0-07.2015

EUREKA MATH™

2. Jose bought $3\frac{1}{5}$ kg of carrots, $1\frac{3}{4}$ kg of potatoes, and $2\frac{2}{5}$ kg of broccoli. What's the total weight of the vegetables?

I'll use addition to find the total weight of the vegetables.

I can draw a tape diagram and label the parts as carrots, potatoes, and broccoli.

I have to find the total weight of all the vegetables, so I'll label the whole with a question mark.

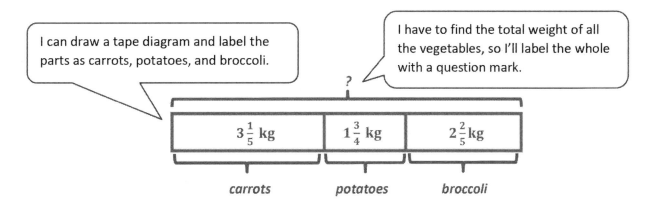

?

| $3\frac{1}{5}$ kg | $1\frac{3}{4}$ kg | $2\frac{2}{5}$ kg |

carrots   potatoes   broccoli

I can add the whole numbers.

$3 + 1 + 2 = 6$

$3\frac{1}{5} + 1\frac{3}{4} + 2\frac{2}{5}$

$= 6 + \frac{1}{5} + \frac{3}{4} + \frac{2}{5}$

$= 6 + \frac{4}{20} + \frac{15}{20} + \frac{8}{20}$

$= 6 + \frac{27}{20}$

$= 6 + \frac{20}{20} + \frac{7}{20}$

$= 7\frac{7}{20}$

I need to rename the fractions with a common unit of twentieths.

$\frac{1}{5} = \frac{4}{20}, \frac{3}{4} = \frac{15}{20},$ and $\frac{2}{5} = \frac{8}{20}.$

$\frac{27}{20} = \frac{20}{20} + \frac{7}{20} = 1\frac{7}{20}$

The total weight of the vegetables is $7\frac{7}{20}$ kilograms.

©2015 Great Minds. eureka-math.org
G5-M1-HWH-1.3.0-07.2015

G5-M3-Lesson 16

> I know $\frac{1}{4}$ plus $\frac{3}{4}$ is equal to $\frac{4}{4}$, or 1.

Draw the following ribbons.

a. 1 ribbon. The piece shown below is only $\frac{1}{4}$ of the whole. Complete the drawing to show the whole ribbon.

> This is 1 unit of $\frac{1}{4}$.

> I can draw 3 more units of $\frac{1}{4}$ to complete the whole.

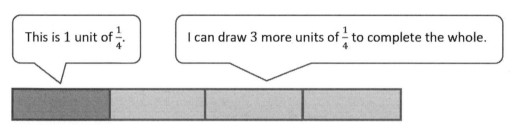

b. 1 ribbon. The piece shown below is $\frac{3}{5}$ of the whole. Complete the drawing to show the whole ribbon.

> I can partition the shaded unit into 3 equal parts.

> I know $\frac{3}{5}$ plus $\frac{2}{5}$ is equal to $\frac{5}{5}$, or 1.

> I need to draw 2 more units to make a total of 5 parts. Now, the shaded part represents $\frac{3}{5}$, and the unshaded part represents $\frac{2}{5}$.

c. 2 ribbons, A and B. One sixth of A is equal to all of B. Draw a picture of the ribbons.

> I know that ribbon A must be longer than B. More specifically, ribbon B is just 1 sixth of A. This also means that ribbon A is 6 times longer than ribbon B.

> I can draw one large unit to represent ribbon A. Then, I can partition it into 6 equal parts.

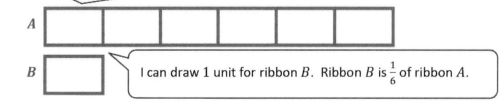

> I can draw 1 unit for ribbon B. Ribbon B is $\frac{1}{6}$ of ribbon A.

EUREKA
MATH™

Homework Helpers

Grade 5
Module 4

G5-M4-Lesson 1

1. A group of students measured the height of their bean sprout to the nearest quarter inch. Draw a line plot to represent their data:

$$2\frac{1}{2}, \quad 1\frac{1}{4}, \quad 2, \quad 3\frac{1}{2}, \quad 2\frac{1}{4}, \quad 2, \quad 2\frac{1}{2}, \quad 2, \quad 2\frac{1}{2}, \quad 2\frac{1}{4}, \quad 3\frac{1}{4}$$

> I can put an X above the number line for each measurement in this set of data.

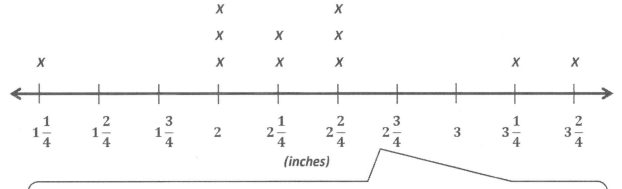

Bean Sprout Height

(inches)

> Since the data set includes values of both half, quarter, and whole inches, I can draw a number line that shows values between $1\frac{1}{4}$ and $3\frac{2}{4}$ and all of the $\frac{1}{4}$ inches in between.

2. Answer the following questions.

> Once my line plot is created, I can use it to help me answer these questions.

   a. Which bean sprout is the tallest?

   The tallest sprout is $3\frac{1}{2}$ inches.

   b. Which bean sprout is the shortest?

   $1\frac{1}{4}$ inches.

> *Most frequent* means the value listed the most times. Since both 2 and $2\frac{1}{2}$ were listed three times, both values are considered most frequent.

   c. Which measurement is the most frequent?

   The most frequent values are 2 inches and $2\frac{1}{2}$ inches.

EUREKA MATH™   Lesson 1:   Measure and compare pencil lengths to the nearest $\frac{1}{2}, \frac{1}{4}$, and $\frac{1}{8}$ of an inch,   1
                              and analyze the data through line plots.

©2015 Great Minds. eureka-math.org
G5-M1-HWH-1.3.0-07.2015

d. What is the total height of all the bean sprouts?

The total height of all the values is 26 inches.

I made sure to add all eleven values. For example, I had to add 2 three times. I checked my answer by adding the values in the list and then the values on the number line to make sure both sums were the same.

Lesson 1: Measure and compare pencil lengths to the nearest $\frac{1}{2}$, $\frac{1}{4}$, and $\frac{1}{8}$ of an inch, and analyze the data through line plots.

©2015 Great Minds. eureka-math.org
G5-M1-HWH-1.3.0-07.2015

EUREKA MATH

G5-M4-Lesson 2

1. Draw a picture to show the division. Express your answer as a fraction.

   a. $1 \div 3 = \mathbf{3\ thirds} \div 3 = \mathbf{1\ third} = \frac{1}{3}$

   > $3 \div 3 = 1$
   > Therefore, 3 thirds ÷ 3 = 1 third.

   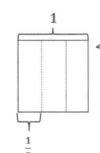

   > I can think about $1 \div 3$ as 1 cracker being shared equally by 3 people. Each person gets $\frac{1}{3}$ of the cracker.

   b. $2 \div 5 = \mathbf{10\ fifths} \div 5 = \mathbf{2\ fifths} = \frac{2}{5}$

   > $10 \div 5 = 2$
   > Therefore, 10 fifths ÷ 5 = 2 fifths.

   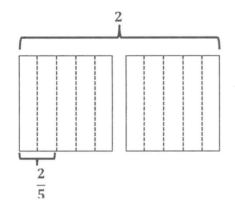

   > If 2 crackers were shared equally by 5 people, each person would get $\frac{2}{5}$ of a cracker.

2. Fill in the blanks to make true number sentences.

   a. $15 \div 4 = \frac{15}{4}$

   > I can write a division expression as a fraction.

   b. $\frac{5}{3} = \underline{\ 5\ } \div \underline{\ 3\ }$

   > I can interpret a fraction as a division expression.

   c. $2\frac{1}{2} = \underline{\ 5\ } \div \underline{\ 2\ }$

   > I can express this mixed number as a fraction greater than 1.
   > $2\frac{1}{2} = \frac{5}{2}$

   > If 5 crackers were shared equally by 2 people, each person would get 5 halves, or $2\frac{1}{2}$ crackers.

©2015 Great Minds. eureka-math.org
G5-M1-HWH-1.3.0-07.2015

G5-M4-Lesson 3

1. Fill in the chart.

Division Expression	Unit Form	Improper Fraction	Mixed Number	Standard Algorithm (Write your answer in whole numbers and fractional units. Then check.)
a. $3 \div 2$	6 *halves* $\div 2 =$ 3 *halves*	$\dfrac{3}{2}$	$1\dfrac{1}{2}$	$1\dfrac{1}{2}$ $2 \overline{)\; 3\;}$ -2 1 *Check:* $2 \times 1\dfrac{1}{2}$ $= 1\dfrac{1}{2} + 1\dfrac{1}{2}$ $= 3$

I can visualize the drawings I made in the previous lesson. 3 crackers are shared equally by 2 people. I could partition each cracker into 2 equal parts and then share the 6 halves.

$3 = 6$ halves

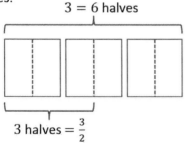

3 halves $= \dfrac{3}{2}$

I can think of this another way too. Since there are 3 crackers being shared equally by 2 people, each person could get 1 whole cracker and $\dfrac{1}{2}$ of another.

3

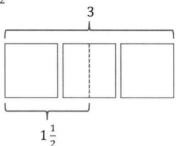

$1\dfrac{1}{2}$

EUREKA MATH

©2015 Great Minds. eureka-math.org
G5-M1-HWH-1.3.0-07.2015

Division Expression	Unit Form	Improper Fraction	Mixed Numbers	Standard Algorithm (Write your answer in whole numbers and fractional units. Then check.)
b. $5 \div 3$	15 *thirds* $\div 3 =$ 5 *thirds*	$\frac{5}{3}$	$1\frac{2}{3}$	$3 \overline{\smash{\big)}\ 5}$ with $1\frac{2}{3}$ on top, -3, 2. Check: $3 \times 1\frac{2}{3}$ $= 1\frac{2}{3} + 1\frac{2}{3} + 1\frac{2}{3}$ $= 3\frac{6}{3}$ $= 3 + 2$ $= 5$

This time I am given the mixed number. I know that $1\frac{2}{3}$ is the same as $\frac{3}{3} + \frac{2}{3}$, which is equal to $\frac{5}{3}$.

I can think of $\frac{5}{3}$ as a division expression, $5 \div 3$.

The standard algorithm makes sense. If there were 5 crackers being shared equally by 3 people, each person could get 1 whole cracker, and then the remaining 2 crackers would be partitioned into 3 equal parts and shared as thirds.

I can visualize one way to model this scenario:

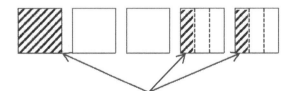

Each person gets 1 whole cracker and $\frac{2}{3}$ of a cracker.

G5-M4-Lesson 4

Draw a tape diagram to solve. Express your answer as a fraction. Show the addition sentence to support your answer.

$5 \div 4 = \frac{5}{4} = 1\frac{1}{4}$

I can think of the expression $5 \div 4$ as 5 crackers being shared equally by 4 people. This unit here represents how much 1 person gets.

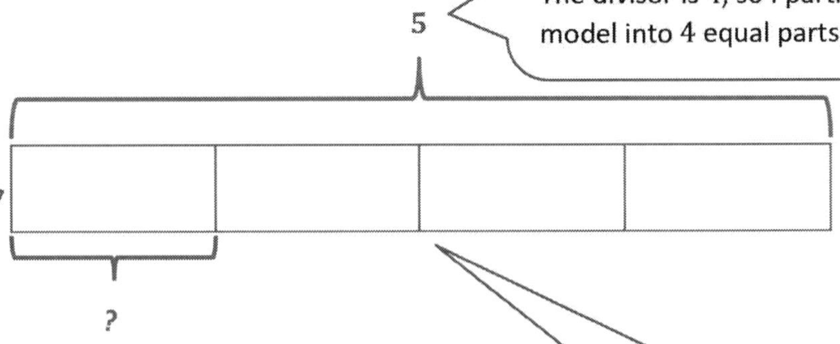

I can model $5 \div 4$ by drawing a tape diagram. The whole tape represents the dividend, 5. The divisor is 4, so I partition the model into 4 equal parts, or units.

5

?

4 *units* = 5

1 *unit* = $5 \div 4 = \frac{5}{4} = 1\frac{1}{4}$

Now that I've divided, I know that each of these four units has a value of $1\frac{1}{4}$.

My tape diagram shows me that the 4 parts, or units, are equal to 5. So, I can find the value of 1 unit by dividing, $5 \div 4$.

$$\begin{array}{r} 1\frac{1}{4} \\ 4 \overline{\smash{)}5} \\ -4 \\ \hline 1 \end{array}$$

Check:

$4 \times 1\frac{1}{4}$

$= 1\frac{1}{4} + 1\frac{1}{4} + 1\frac{1}{4} + 1\frac{1}{4}$

$= 4 + \frac{4}{4}$

$= 5$

Lesson 4: Use tape diagrams to model fractions as division.

EUREKA MATH

G5-M4-Lesson 5

Kenneth divided 15 cups of whole wheat flour equally to make 4 loaves of bread.

a. How much whole wheat flour went into each loaf?

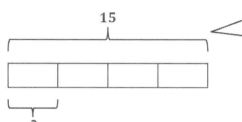

The whole tape represents 15 cups of flour. Since the flour is used to make 4 equal loaves of bread, I partitioned the tape into 4 equal units, or parts.

4 units = 15

$1 \ unit = 15 \div 4 = \frac{15}{4} = 3\frac{3}{4}$

$\frac{15}{4}$ is equal to $\frac{4}{4} + \frac{4}{4} + \frac{4}{4} + \frac{3}{4}$, which is the same as $3\frac{3}{4}$.

Kenneth used $3\frac{3}{4}$ cups of whole wheat flour for each loaf of bread.

b. How many cups of whole wheat flour are in 3 loaves of bread?

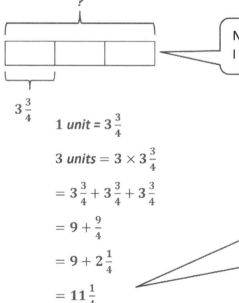

Now that I know how much flour is in one loaf of bread, I can multiply that amount by 3 to answer this question.

$1 \ unit = 3\frac{3}{4}$

$3 \ units = 3 \times 3\frac{3}{4}$

$= 3\frac{3}{4} + 3\frac{3}{4} + 3\frac{3}{4}$

$= 9 + \frac{9}{4}$

$= 9 + 2\frac{1}{4}$

$= 11\frac{1}{4}$

Since Kenneth used a total of 15 cups of flour for 4 loaves, I could have also used subtraction to find the amount used in 3 loaves.

$15 - 3\frac{3}{4} = 12 - \frac{3}{4} = 11\frac{1}{4}$

There are $11\frac{1}{4}$ cups of whole wheat flour in 3 loaves.

EUREKA
MATH™

Lesson 5:   Solve word problems involving division of whole numbers with answers
            in the form of fractions or whole numbers.

7

©2015 Great Minds. eureka-math.org
G5-M1-HWH-1.3.0-07.2015

G5-M4-Lesson 6

1. Find the value of the following.

```
*  |  *  |  *
*  |  *  |  *
*  |  *  |  *
*  |  *  |  *
*  |  *  |  *
```

> The array shows a total of 15 stars. Each column represents 1 third.

$\frac{1}{3}$ *of* $15 = 5$

> To find 2 thirds, I can count the number of stars in two columns.

$\frac{2}{3}$ *of* $15 = 10$

$\frac{3}{3}$ *of* $15 = 15$

> $\frac{3}{3}$ represents *all* of the stars, or the amount found in all 3 columns.

2. Find $\frac{3}{4}$ of 12. Draw a set, and shade to show your thinking.

> The total in the array has to be 12. Since I'm trying to find fourths, I can draw a row of 4 circles. I can draw a second row of 4 circles and continue drawing rows until I have a total of 12 circles.

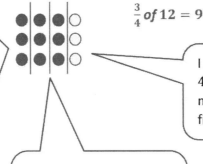

$\frac{3}{4}$ *of* $12 = 9$

> I shaded 3 out of the 4 columns. I counted how many circles I shaded to find the answer.

> I drew vertical lines to clearly show the fourths. Each column represents $\frac{1}{4}$ of 12.

EUREKA MATH

3. How does knowing $\frac{1}{3}$ of 18 help you find $\frac{2}{3}$ of 18? Draw a picture to explain your thinking.

> I know I need a set of 18. Since I'm finding a third of 18, I drew rows of 3.

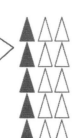

From my drawing, I know $\frac{1}{3}$ of 18 is 6.

$\frac{2}{3}$ of 18 is twice as much as $\frac{1}{3}$ of 18.

$\frac{2}{3}$ of 18 = 12.

> $\frac{1}{3}$ of 18 is 6, so $\frac{2}{3}$ of 18 is 2 × 6, or 12.
>
> $\frac{3}{3}$ of 18 would be 3 × 6, or 18.

4. Michael collected 21 sports cards. $\frac{3}{7}$ of the cards are baseball cards. How many cards are not baseball cards?

> The whole set is 21 cards. In order to show sevenths, I can draw 7 rectangles in a column and then continue drawing columns until I show all 21 cards.

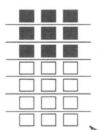

12 of the cards are not baseball cards.

> I drew horizontal lines to show the sevenths. I shaded in $\frac{3}{7}$ to show the collection of baseball cards.

> The question asked how many cards were *not* baseball cards, so I counted $\frac{4}{7}$, or 12, rectangles to get my answer.

> In the other examples, I drew rows first. In this question, I drew columns first. Either way is correct, and either way will show my thinking accurately.

G5-M4-Lesson 7

Solve using a tape diagram.

> I can draw a tape diagram and label the whole as 25. I need to find fifths, so I partition the whole into five units, or parts.

a. $\frac{1}{5}$ of $25 = 5$

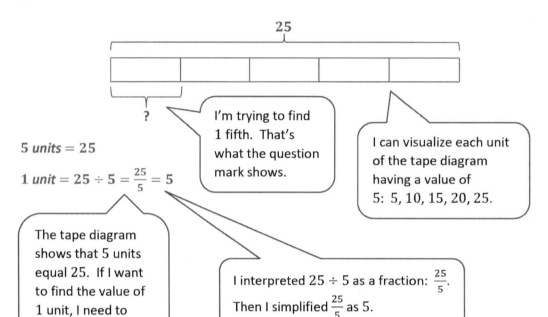

25

?

5 *units* = 25

1 *unit* = $25 \div 5 = \frac{25}{5} = 5$

> I'm trying to find 1 fifth. That's what the question mark shows.

> I can visualize each unit of the tape diagram having a value of 5: 5, 10, 15, 20, 25.

> The tape diagram shows that 5 units equal 25. If I want to find the value of 1 unit, I need to divide 25 by 5.

> I interpreted $25 \div 5$ as a fraction: $\frac{25}{5}$. Then I simplified $\frac{25}{5}$ as 5.

b. $\frac{3}{4} \times 16 = 12$

> I can interpret $\frac{3}{4} \times 16$ as $\frac{3}{4}$ of 16.

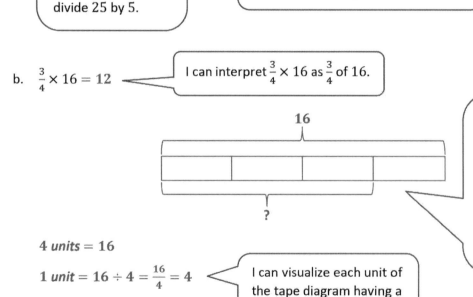

16

?

4 *units* = 16

1 *unit* = $16 \div 4 = \frac{16}{4} = 4$

3 *units* = $3 \times 4 = 12$

> The tape diagram shows the whole as 16 partitioned into 4 parts. I found the value of one unit and then multiplied that by three to find the value of 3 units.

> I can visualize each unit of the tape diagram having a value of 4: 4, 8, 12, 16.

Lesson 7:   Multiply any whole number by a fraction using tape diagrams.   EUREKA MATH

I can interpret this as $\frac{5}{6}$ of ? = 25.

c. $\frac{5}{6}$ of a number is 25. What's the number?

In this problem, I am given the value of some parts, and I need to find the value of the whole.

?

25

$\frac{5}{6}$ = 25, so these 5 units have a value of 25. If I can find the value of 1 unit, I can find the value of 6 units, or the whole.

5 *units* = 25

1 *unit* = $25 \div 5 = \frac{25}{5} = 5$

6 *units* = $6 \times 5 = 30$

I can visualize each unit of the tape diagram having a value of 5: 5, 10, 15, 20, 25, 30.

The number is 30.

G5-M4-Lesson 8

1. Rewrite the following expressions as shown in the example.

Example: $\frac{4}{7}+\frac{4}{7}+\frac{4}{7}=\frac{3\times 4}{7}=\frac{12}{7}$

> This expression is repeatedly adding 2 fifths. I can write it as a multiplication expression.
>
> This is the same as $4\times\frac{2}{5}$, or $\frac{4\times 2}{5}$.

a. $\frac{3}{2}+\frac{3}{2}+\frac{3}{2}$

$\frac{3}{2}+\frac{3}{2}+\frac{3}{2}=\frac{3\times 3}{2}=\frac{9}{2}$

b. $\frac{2}{5}+\frac{2}{5}+\frac{2}{5}+\frac{2}{5}$

$\frac{2}{5}+\frac{2}{5}+\frac{2}{5}+\frac{2}{5}=\frac{4\times 2}{5}=\frac{8}{5}$

2. Solve each problem in two different ways. Express your answer in simplest form.

a. $\frac{2}{5}\times 30$

$\frac{2}{5}\times 30=\frac{2\times 30}{5}=\frac{60}{5}=12$

> In this method, I simplified after I multiplied.

$\frac{2}{5}\times 30=\frac{2\times \cancel{30}^{6}}{\cancel{5}_{1}}=12$

> In this method, I see that 30 and 5 have a common factor of 5. I can divide both 30 and 5 by 5, and now I can think of the fraction as $\frac{2\times 6}{1}$.

> This method involved some larger numbers that are challenging to do mentally.

> Dividing by a common factor of 8 made this method much simpler! I can do this mentally.

b. $32\times\frac{7}{8}$

$32\times\frac{7}{8}=\frac{32\times 7}{8}=\frac{224}{8}=28$

$32\times\frac{7}{8}=\frac{\cancel{32}^{4}\times 7}{\cancel{8}_{1}}=28$

3. Solve any way you choose.

$\frac{3}{4}\times 60$

$\frac{3}{4}\times 60=\frac{3\times 60}{4}=\frac{180}{4}=45$

$\frac{3}{4}$ hour = ___ minutes

$\frac{3}{4}$ *hour = 45 minutes*

> Since there are 60 minutes in an hour, this is the expression I can use to find how many minutes are in $\frac{3}{4}$ of an hour.

> I could have solved by simplifying before I multiplied.
>
> $\frac{3}{4}\times 60=\frac{3\times \cancel{60}^{15}}{\cancel{4}_{1}}=45$

Lesson 8:   Relate a fraction of a set to the repeated addition interpretation of fraction multiplication.

EUREKA MATH

G5-M4-Lesson 9

1. Convert. Show your work using a tape diagram or an equation.

    a. $\frac{3}{4}$ year = _____ months

    $\frac{3}{4}$ year = $\frac{3}{4} \times 1$ year

    I can think of $\frac{3}{4}$ year as $\frac{3}{4}$ of 1 year.

    $= \frac{3}{4} \times 12$ months

    I can rename 1 year as 12 months.

    $= \frac{36}{4}$ months

    I can do this in my head: $\frac{3}{4} \times 12 = \frac{3 \times 12}{4} = \frac{36}{4}$.

    $= 9$ months

    b. $\frac{5}{6}$ hour = _____ minutes

    $\frac{5}{6}$ hour = $\frac{5}{6} \times 1$ hour

    $= \frac{5}{6} \times 60$ minutes

    $= \frac{300}{6}$ minutes

    $= 50$ minutes

    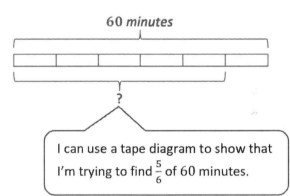

    60 minutes

    I can use a tape diagram to show that I'm trying to find $\frac{5}{6}$ of 60 minutes.

2. $\frac{2}{3}$ of a yardstick was painted blue. How many feet of the yardstick were painted blue?

    $\frac{2}{3}$ yard = _____ feet

    $= \frac{2}{3} \times 1$ yard

    $= \frac{2}{3} \times 3$ feet

    $= \frac{6}{3}$ feet

    $= 2$ feet

    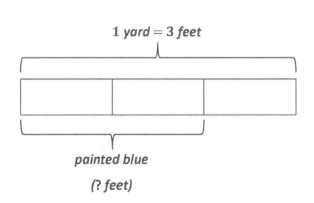

    1 yard = 3 feet

    painted blue
    (? feet)

    2 feet of the yardstick are painted blue.

G5-M4-Lesson 10

> *Evaluate* means *solve*, so I need to find the value of the unknown.

1. Write expressions to match the diagrams. Then, evaluate.

    a.

    > I also could have written $(23 - 8) \times \frac{1}{3}$.
    >
    > Both expressions are correct.

    $\frac{1}{3} \times (23 - 8)$

    $= \frac{1}{3} \times 15$

    $= \frac{15}{3}$

    $= 5$

    > 23 − 8, or 15, is the whole.

    23 − 8

    ?

    > The question mark shows that I'm trying to find 1 third of the whole.

    > The question mark tells me I need to find the value of the whole.

    b.

    $4 \times \left(\frac{4}{5} - \frac{1}{3}\right)$

    $= 4 \times \left(\frac{12}{15} - \frac{5}{15}\right)$

    $= 4 \times \frac{7}{15}$

    $= \frac{28}{15}$

    $= 1\frac{13}{15}$

    ?

    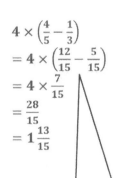

    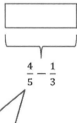

    $\frac{4}{5} - \frac{1}{3}$

    > This 1 unit is equal to $\frac{1}{4}$ of the whole. If I multiply it by 4, I can find the value of the whole.

    > In order to subtract, I need to make like units.

    > I have to find the difference before I multiply by 4.

Lesson 10:   Compare and evaluate expressions with parentheses.

©2015 Great Minds. eureka-math.org
G5-M1-HWH-1.3.0-07.2015

EUREKA
MATH

2. Circle the expression(s) that give the same product as $4 \times \frac{2}{5}$. Explain how you know.

   a. $5 \div (2 \times 4)$

      This expression is equal to $5 \div 8$, not $8 \div 5$.

   b. $\left(2 \div 5 \times 4 \right)$

      $2 \div 5$ *is equal to* $\frac{2}{5}$. $\frac{2}{5} \times 4 = 4 \times \frac{2}{5}$

> I can determine which expressions are equivalent to $4 \times \frac{2}{5}$ without evaluating. However, to check my thinking, I can solve.
> $4 \times \frac{2}{5} = \frac{4 \times 2}{5} = \frac{8}{5} = 1\frac{3}{5}$

   c. $\left(4 \times 2 \div 5 \right)$

      This expression is equal to $8 \div 5$, which is $\frac{8}{5}$ or $1\frac{3}{5}$.

   d. $4 \times \frac{5}{2}$

      This expression does have 4 as one of the factors, but $\frac{5}{2}$ is not equivalent to $\frac{2}{5}$.

3. Write an expression to match, and then evaluate.

   a. $\frac{1}{3}$ the sum of 12 and 21

> The word *sum* tells me that 12 and 21 are being added.

> In order to find $\frac{1}{3}$ of the sum, I can multiply by $\frac{1}{3}$ or divide by 3.

$$\frac{1}{3} \times (12 + 21)$$
$$= \frac{1}{3} \times 33$$
$$= \frac{33}{3}$$
$$= 11$$

   b. Subtract 5 from $\frac{1}{7}$ of 49.

> I need to be careful with subtraction! Even though the beginning of the expression says to subtract 5, I need to find $\frac{1}{7}$ of 49 first.

$$\frac{1}{7} \times 49 - 5$$
$$= \frac{49}{7} - 5$$
$$= 7 - 5$$
$$= 2$$

©2015 Great Minds. eureka-math.org
G5-M1-HWH-1.3.0-07.2015

4. Use $<, >,$ or $=$ to make true number sentences without calculating. Explain your thinking.

a. $(17 \times 41) + \frac{5}{4}$ $\left(\ <\ \right)$ $\frac{7}{4} + (17 \times 41)$

Since both expressions show (17×41), I only have to compare the parts being added to this product.

$\frac{5}{4} < \frac{7}{4}$. Therefore, the expression on the left is less than the expression on the right.

In both expressions, one of the factors is $\frac{3}{4}$. I only have to compare the other factors.

I know that $15 + 18 = 33$ and $3 \times 11 = 33$. The second factors are equivalent too.

b. $\frac{3}{4} \times (15 + 18)$ $\left(\ =\ \right)$ $(3 \times 11) \times \frac{3}{4}$

Since both factors are equivalent, these expressions are equal.

EUREKA
MATH

G5-M4-Lesson 11

Use the RDW (Read, Draw, Write) method to solve.

1. Janice and Adam cooked a 1 lb package of spinach. Janice ate $\frac{1}{2}$ of the spinach, and Adam ate $\frac{1}{4}$ of the spinach. What fraction of the package was left? How many ounces were left?

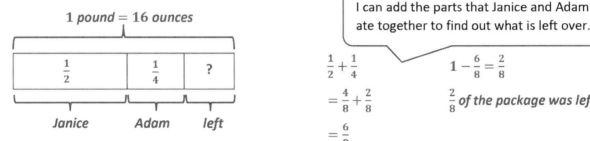

I can add the parts that Janice and Adam ate together to find out what is left over.

$$\frac{1}{2} + \frac{1}{4}$$
$$= \frac{4}{8} + \frac{2}{8}$$
$$= \frac{6}{8}$$

$$1 - \frac{6}{8} = \frac{2}{8}$$

$\frac{2}{8}$ of the package was left.

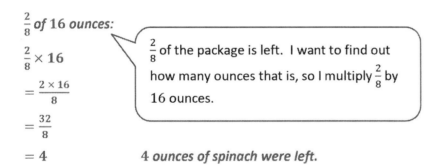

$\frac{2}{8}$ of 16 ounces:

$\frac{2}{8} \times 16$

$= \frac{2 \times 16}{8}$

$= \frac{32}{8}$

$= 4$

$\frac{2}{8}$ of the package is left. I want to find out how many ounces that is, so I multiply $\frac{2}{8}$ by 16 ounces.

4 ounces of spinach were left.

2. Using the tape diagram below, create a story problem about a school. Your story must include a fraction.

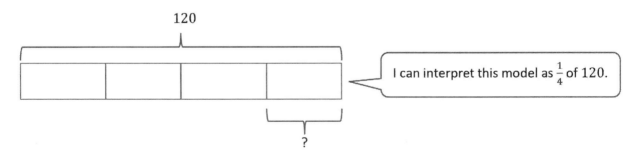

I can interpret this model as $\frac{1}{4}$ of 120.

Crestview Elementary School has 120 fifth graders. Three-fourths of them ride the bus to school. The rest of the fifth-grade students walk to school. What fraction of the fifth-grade students walk to school?

EUREKA MATH

Lesson 11:   Solve and create fraction word problems involving addition, subtraction and multiplication.

©2015 Great Minds. eureka-math.org
G5-M1-HWH-1.3.0-07.2015

G5-M4-Lesson 12

Solve using the RDW (Read, Draw, Write) method.

1. Beth ran her leg of a relay race in $\frac{3}{5}$ the amount of time it took Margaret. Wayne ran his leg of the relay race in $\frac{2}{3}$ the time it took Beth. Margaret finished the race in 30 minutes. How long did it take for Wayne to finish his part of the race?

30

Margaret

Since Beth's time was $\frac{3}{5}$ of Margaret's, I can partition Margaret's time into 5 equal units. Now I can show that Beth's time is $\frac{3}{5}$ of Margaret's.

Beth

Wayne

Wayne's time was $\frac{2}{3}$ of Beth's time. 3 units represent Beth's time, so I can show Wayne's time with 2 units. $\frac{2}{3}$ of 3 units is 2 units.

5 units = 30

1 unit = 30 ÷ 5 = 6

I can use my tape diagram to help me solve. I know that Margaret finished in 30 minutes; therefore, the 5 units representing Margaret's time are equal to 30 minutes.

I can visualize each unit in the tape diagram being equal to 6 minutes.

2 units = 2 × 6 = 12

Wayne finished the race in 12 minutes.

Wayne's time is equal to 2 units of 6 minutes each, or 12 minutes.

2. Create a story problem about a brother and sister and the money they spend at a deli whose solution is given by the expression $\frac{1}{3} \times (7 + 8)$.

Two siblings went to a deli. The sister had $7.00, and her brother had $8.00. They spent one-third of their combined money. How much money did they spend in the deli?

The parentheses tell me to add first. In my story problem, I wrote that the siblings combined their money.

Lesson 12:   Solve and create fraction word problems involving addition, subtraction and multiplication.

EUREKA MATH

G5-M4-Lesson 13

1. Solve. Draw a rectangular fraction model to show your thinking.

    a.   Half of $\frac{1}{4}$ pan of brownies

    Half of $\frac{1}{4} = \frac{1}{8}$

    $$\frac{1}{2} \times \frac{1}{4} = \frac{1}{8}$$

    > The problem tells me I have $\frac{1}{4}$ pan of brownies. I can draw a whole pan. Then, I can shade and label $\frac{1}{4}$ of the pan.

    > Seeing the word *of* reminds me of third grade when I learned that 2×3 meant 2 groups *of* 3.

    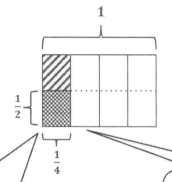

    > Since I want to model 1 half of the fourth of a pan, I can partition the fourth into 2 equal parts, or halves. I can shade $\frac{1}{2}$ of the $\frac{1}{4}$.

    > My model shows me that $\frac{1}{2}$ of $\frac{1}{4}$ is equal to $\frac{1}{8}$ of the pan of brownies.

    b. $\frac{1}{4} \times \frac{1}{4}$

    $$\frac{1}{4} \times \frac{1}{4} = \frac{1}{16}$$

    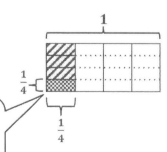

    > The part that is double-shaded shows $\frac{1}{4}$ of $\frac{1}{4}$.
    >
    > $$\frac{1}{4} \text{ of } \frac{1}{4} = \frac{1}{16}$$

2. The Guerra family uses $\frac{3}{4}$ of their backyard for a pool. $\frac{1}{3}$ of the remaining yard is used for a vegetable garden. The rest of the yard is grass. What fraction of the entire backyard is for the vegetable garden? Draw a picture to support your answer.

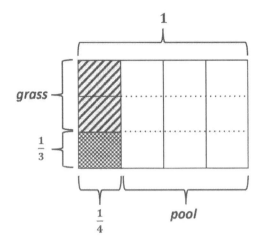

Since $\frac{3}{4}$ of the backyard is a pool, that means $\frac{1}{4}$ of the backyard is *not* a pool.

$$\frac{1}{3} \times \frac{1}{4} = \frac{1}{12}$$

$\frac{1}{12}$ *of the backyard is a vegetable garden.*

EUREKA
MATH™

©2015 Great Minds. eureka-math.org
G5-M1-HWH-1.3.0-07.2015

G5-M4-Lesson 14

1. Solve. Draw a rectangular fraction model to explain your thinking.

    a. $\frac{1}{3}$ of $\frac{3}{5}$ = $\frac{1}{3}$ of ___3___ fifths = ___1___ fifth

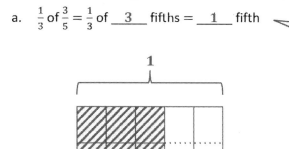

$\frac{1}{3}$ of 3 is 1.

$\frac{1}{3}$ of 3 bananas is 1 banana.

$\frac{1}{3}$ of 3 fifths is 1 fifth.

$\frac{1}{3} \times \frac{3}{5} = \frac{3}{15} = \frac{1}{5}$

I can model $\frac{3}{5}$ by partitioning vertically first. Then to show $\frac{1}{3}$ of $\frac{3}{5}$, I can partition with horizontal lines.

b. $\frac{1}{2} \times \frac{3}{4}$

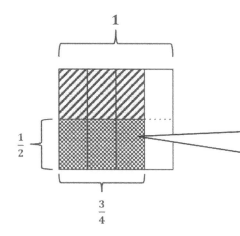

$\frac{1}{2} \times \frac{3}{4} = \frac{3}{8}$

My model shows me that $\frac{1}{2}$ of $\frac{3}{4}$ is $\frac{3}{8}$. The part here that is double-shaded shows the product, 3 eighths.

2. Kenny collects coins. $\frac{3}{5}$ of his collection is dimes. $\frac{1}{2}$ of the remaining coins are quarters. What fraction of Kenny's whole collection is quarters? Support your answer with a model.

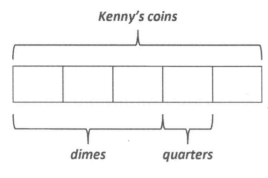

Since $\frac{3}{5}$ of Kenny's collection is dimes, then $\frac{2}{5}$ of the collection is not dimes. 1 half of that $\frac{2}{5}$ is quarters. $\frac{1}{2}$ of $\frac{2}{5}$ is $\frac{1}{5}$.

$$\frac{1}{2} \times \frac{2}{5} = \frac{2}{10} = \frac{1}{5}$$

One fifth of Kenny's coin collection is quarters.

3. In Jan's class, $\frac{3}{8}$ of the students take the bus to school. $\frac{4}{5}$ of the non-bus riders walk to school. One half of the remaining students ride their bikes to school.

   a. What fraction of all the students walk to school?

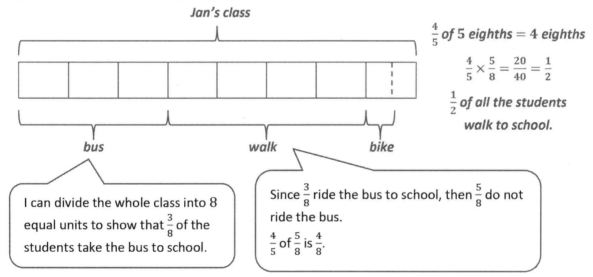

$\frac{4}{5}$ *of 5 eighths = 4 eighths*

$$\frac{4}{5} \times \frac{5}{8} = \frac{20}{40} = \frac{1}{2}$$

$\frac{1}{2}$ *of all the students walk to school.*

I can divide the whole class into 8 equal units to show that $\frac{3}{8}$ of the students take the bus to school.

Since $\frac{3}{8}$ ride the bus to school, then $\frac{5}{8}$ do not ride the bus.
$\frac{4}{5}$ of $\frac{5}{8}$ is $\frac{4}{8}$.

   b. What fraction of all the students ride their bikes to school?

$\frac{1}{2}$ *of* $\frac{1}{8} = \frac{1}{16}$

$\frac{1}{16}$ *of all the students bike to school.*

After labeling the units that represent the students that walk or bus to school, there was only 1 unit, or $\frac{1}{8}$ of the class, remaining. Half of those students bike to school.

Lesson 14:   Multiply unit fractions by non-unit fractions.

G5-M4-Lesson 15

1. Solve. Draw a rectangular fraction model to explain your thinking. Then, write a multiplication sentence.

$\frac{2}{5}$ of $\frac{2}{3}$

$\frac{2}{5} \times \frac{2}{3} = \frac{4}{15}$

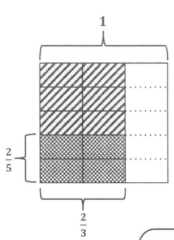

2. Multiply.

a. $\frac{3}{8} \times \frac{2}{5}$

> The 2 in the numerator and the 8 in the denominator have a common factor of 2.
>
> $2 \div 2 = 1$ and $8 \div 2 = 4$

$\frac{3}{8} \times \frac{2}{5} = \frac{3 \times 2}{8 \times 5} = \frac{3}{20}$

> Now the numerator is 3×1, and the denominator is 4×5.

b. $\frac{2}{5} \times \frac{10}{12}$

> I was able to rename this fraction twice before multiplying. 5 and 10 have a common factor of 5.

$\frac{2}{5} \times \frac{10}{12} = \frac{2 \times 10}{5 \times 12} = \frac{2}{6}$

> And 2 and 12 have a common factor of 2.

> Now the numerator is 1×2, and the denominator is 1×6.

G5-M4-Lesson 16

Solve and show your thinking with a tape diagram.

1. Heidi had 6 pounds of tomatoes from her garden. She used $\frac{3}{4}$ of all the tomatoes to make sauce and gave $\frac{2}{3}$ of the rest of the tomatoes to her neighbor. How many ounces of tomatoes did Heidi give to her neighbor?

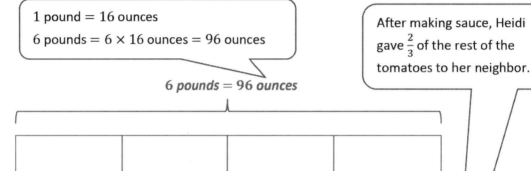

1 pound = 16 ounces
6 pounds = 6 × 16 ounces = 96 ounces

After making sauce, Heidi gave $\frac{2}{3}$ of the rest of the tomatoes to her neighbor.

6 pounds = 96 ounces

sauce   rest

My tape diagram shows me that the total value of the 4 units is 96 ounces. I can divide to find the value of 1 unit, or $\frac{1}{4}$ of 96.

neighbor
(? ounces)

4 *units* = 96

1 *unit* = 96 ÷ 4 = 24

Now I know that Heidi had 24 ounces of tomatoes left after making sauce.

When I look at my model, I can think of this another way. Heidi gave $\frac{2}{3}$ of $\frac{1}{4}$ to her neighbor.

$\frac{2}{3} \times \frac{1}{4} = \frac{2}{12} = \frac{1}{6}$

Heidi gave $\frac{1}{6}$ of all the tomatoes to her neighbor.

$\frac{2}{3}$ *of* 24 = $\frac{2 \times 24}{3} = \frac{48}{3} = 16$

I can find $\frac{2}{3}$ of 24 and know how many ounces Heidi gave to her neighbor.

$\frac{1}{6}$ of 96 = 16

Heidi gave her neighbor 16 *ounces of tomatoes.*

Lesson 16:   Solve word problems using tape diagrams and fraction-by-fraction
                        multiplication.

©2015 Great Minds. eureka-math.org
G5-M1-HWH-1.3.0-07.2015

**EUREKA
MATH**

2. Tracey spent $\frac{2}{3}$ of her money on movie tickets and $\frac{3}{4}$ of the remaining money on popcorn and water. If she had $4 left over, how much money did she have at first?

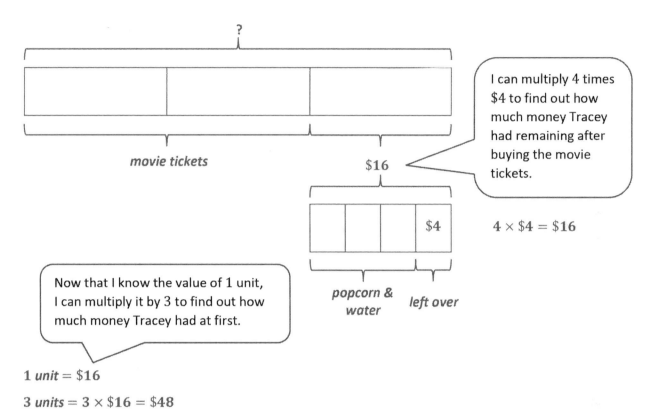

movie tickets

$16

I can multiply 4 times $4 to find out how much money Tracey had remaining after buying the movie tickets.

$4

$4 \times \$4 = \$16$

popcorn & water   left over

Now that I know the value of 1 unit, I can multiply it by 3 to find out how much money Tracey had at first.

1 unit = $16

3 units = $3 \times \$16 = \$48$

Tracey had $48 at first.

G5-M4-Lesson 17

1. Multiply and model. Rewrite each expression as a multiplication sentence with decimal factors.

a. $\dfrac{3}{10} \times \dfrac{2}{10}$

$= \dfrac{3 \times 2}{10 \times 10}$

$= \dfrac{6}{100}$

Since the whole grid represents 1, each square represents $\dfrac{1}{100}$. 10 squares is equal to $\dfrac{1}{10}$.

When multiplying fractions, I multiply the two numerators, 3×2, and the two denominators, 10×10, to get $\dfrac{6}{100}$.

I shade in $\dfrac{2}{10}$ (20 squares vertically).

I shade in $\dfrac{3}{10}$ of $\dfrac{2}{10}$ (6 squares).

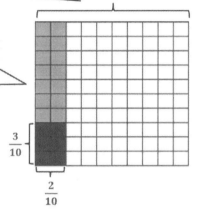

I label each whole grid as 1, and each square represents $\dfrac{1}{100}$.

b. $\dfrac{3}{10} \times 1.2$

$= \dfrac{3}{10} \times \dfrac{12}{10}$

$= \dfrac{3 \times 12}{10 \times 10}$

$= \dfrac{36}{100}$

I shade in 1 and $\dfrac{2}{10}$ (120 squares vertically).

I rename 1.2 as a fraction greater than one, $\dfrac{12}{10}$, and then multiply to get $\dfrac{36}{100}$.

$1.2 = \dfrac{12}{10}$

I shade in $\dfrac{3}{10}$ of $\dfrac{12}{10}$ (36 squares).

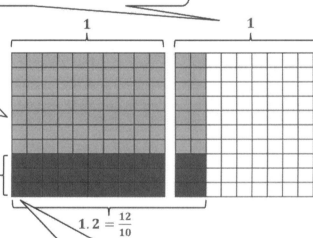

EUREKA
MATH

©2015 Great Minds. eureka-math.org
G5-M1-HWH-1.3.0-07.2015

2. Multiply.

a. 2×0.6

$= 2 \times \frac{6}{10}$

$= \frac{2 \times 6}{10}$

$= \frac{12}{10}$

$= 1.2$

> I rewrite the decimal as a fraction and then multiply the two numerators and the two denominators to get $\frac{12}{10}$. Lastly, I write it as a mixed number if possible.

> 0.02 is 2 hundredths, or $\frac{2}{100}$. After multiplying, the answer is $\frac{12}{1,000}$ or 0.012.

b. 0.2×0.6

$= \frac{2}{10} \times \frac{6}{10}$

$= \frac{2 \times 6}{10 \times 10}$

$= \frac{12}{100}$

$= 0.12$

> 0.2 is 2 tenths, or $\frac{2}{10}$. After multiplying, the answer is $\frac{12}{100}$, or 0.12.

c. 0.02×0.6

$= \frac{2}{100} \times \frac{6}{10}$

$= \frac{2 \times 6}{100 \times 10}$

$= \frac{12}{1,000}$

$= 0.012$

3. Sydney makes 1.2 liters of orange juice. If she pours 4 tenths of the orange juice in the glass, how many liters of orange juice are in the glass?

$\frac{4}{10}$ *of* 1.2 L

$\frac{4}{10} \times 1.2$

$= \frac{4}{10} \times \frac{12}{10}$

$= \frac{4 \times 12}{10 \times 10}$

$= \frac{48}{100}$

$= 0.48$

> To find 4 tenths of 1.2 liters, I multiply $\frac{4}{10}$ times $\frac{12}{10}$ to get $\frac{48}{100}$, or 0.48.

There are 0.48 L *of orange juice in the glass.*

©2015 Great Minds. eureka-math.org
G5-M1-HWH-1.3.0-07.2015

G5-M4-Lesson 18

1. Multiply using both fraction form and unit form.

    a. $2.3 \times 1.6 = \dfrac{23}{10} \times \dfrac{16}{10}$

$$= \dfrac{23 \times 16}{10 \times 10}$$

$$= \dfrac{368}{100}$$

$$= 3.68$$

```
        2   3    tenths
  ×     1,  6    tenths
  ─────────────
        1   3   8
  +  2   3   0
  ─────────────
     3   6   8   hundredths
```

> I write the decimals (2.3 and 1.6) in unit form (23 tenths and 16 tenths).

> I express the decimals (2.3 and 1.6) as fractions ($\frac{23}{10}$ and $\frac{16}{10}$), and then I multiply to get $\frac{368}{100}$, or 3.68.

> I multiply the 2 factors as if they are whole numbers to get 368. The product's unit is hundredths because a tenth times a tenth is equal to a hundredth.

    b. $2.38 \times 1.8 = \dfrac{238}{100} \times \dfrac{18}{10}$

$$= \dfrac{238 \times 18}{100 \times 10}$$

$$= \dfrac{4{,}284}{1{,}000}$$

$$= 4.284$$

```
            2   3   8   hundredths
  ×             1   8   tenths
  ─────────────────────
        1   9   0   4
  +  2   3   8   0
  ─────────────────────
     4,  2   8   4   thousandths
```

> I express the decimals (2.38 and 1.8) in unit form (238 hundredths and 18 tenths).

> A hundredth times a tenth is a thousandth.

EUREKA MATH

2. A flower garden measures 2.75 meters by 4.2 meters.

   a. Find the area of the flower garden.

   $2.75 \text{ m} \times 4.2 \text{ m} = 11.55 \text{ m}^2$

   The area of the flower garden is 11.55 square meters.

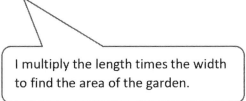

   I multiply the length times the width to find the area of the garden.

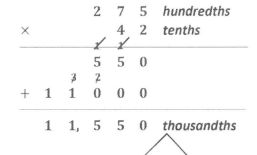

	2	7	5		*hundredths*
×		4	2		*tenths*
	5	5	0		
+ 1	1	0	0	0	
1	1,	5	5	0	*thousandths*

   A hundredth times a tenth is a thousandth.

   $$\frac{1}{100} \times \frac{1}{10} = \frac{1 \times 1}{100 \times 10} = \frac{1}{1,000}$$

   b. The area of the vegetable garden is one and a half times that of the flower garden. Find the total area of the flower garden and the vegetable garden.

   $11.55 \text{ m}^2 \times 1.5 = 17.325 \text{ m}^2$ $11.55 \text{ m}^2 + 17.325 \text{ m}^2 = 28.875 \text{ m}^2$

	1	1	5	5	*hundredths*
×			1	5	*tenths*
	5	7	7	5	
+ 1	1	5	5	0	
1	7,	3	2	5	*thousandths*

	1	1.	5	5	0
+	1	7.	3	2	5
	2	8.	8	7	5

   I add the 2 areas together to find the total area.

   I find the area of the vegetable garden by multiplying the flower garden's area by 1.5, or 15 tenths.

   The total area of the flower garden and the vegetable garden is 28.875 m^2.

G5-M4-Lesson 19

1. Convert. Express your answer as a mixed number, if possible.

    a. 9 in = _____ ft

    $9 \text{ in} = 9 \times 1 \text{ in}$

    $= 9 \times \frac{1}{12} \text{ ft}$

    $= \frac{9}{12} \text{ ft}$

    $= \frac{3}{4} \text{ ft}$

    > I know that 1 foot = 12 inches and 1 inch = $\frac{1}{12}$ foot.

    > 9 inches is equal to 9 times 1 inch. I can rename 1 inch as $\frac{1}{12}$ foot and then multiply.

    b. 20 oz = _____ lb

    $20 \text{ oz} = 20 \times 1 \text{ oz}$

    $= 20 \times \frac{1}{16} \text{ lb}$

    $= \frac{20}{16} \text{ lb}$

    $= 1\frac{4}{16} \text{ lb}$

    $= 1\frac{1}{4} \text{ lb}$

    > I know that 1 pound = 16 ounces and 1 ounce = $\frac{1}{16}$ pound.

    > 20 ounces is equal to 20 times 1 ounce. I can rename 1 ounce as $\frac{1}{16}$ pound and then multiply.

2. Jack buys 14 ounces of peanuts.

    What fraction of a pound of peanuts did Jack buy?

    14 oz = _____ lb

    $14 \text{ oz} = 14 \times 1 \text{ oz}$

    $= 14 \times \frac{1}{16} \text{ lb}$

    $= \frac{14}{16} \text{ lb}$

    $= \frac{7}{8} \text{ lb}$

    > 1 pound = 16 ounces, and 1 ounce = $\frac{1}{16}$ pound.

Jack bought $\frac{7}{8}$ pound of peanuts.

EUREKA MATH™

G5-M4-Lesson 20

Convert. Express the answer as a mixed number.

1. $2\frac{2}{3}$ ft = _____ in

1 foot = 12 inches

$2\frac{2}{3}$ ft $= 2\frac{2}{3} \times 1$ ft

$\qquad = 2\frac{2}{3} \times 12$ in

I rename $2\frac{2}{3}$ as a fraction greater than 1, or an improper fraction, $\frac{8}{3}$. Then, I multiply.

$\qquad = \frac{8}{3} \times 12$ in

$\qquad = \frac{96}{3}$ in

$\qquad = 32$ in

2. $2\frac{7}{10}$ hr = _____ min

1 hour = 60 minutes

$2\frac{7}{10}$ hr $= 2\frac{7}{10} \times 1$ hr

$\qquad = 2\frac{7}{10} \times 60$ min

$\qquad = (2 \times 60 \text{ min}) + \left(\frac{7}{10} \times 60 \text{ min}\right)$

I can use the distributive property. I multiply 2×60 minutes and add that to the product of $\frac{7}{10} \times 60$ minutes.

$\qquad = (120 \text{ min}) + (42 \text{ min})$

$\qquad = 162$ min

©2015 Great Minds. eureka-math.org
G5-M1-HWH-1.3.0-07.2015

3. Charlie buys $2\frac{1}{4}$ pounds of apples for a pie. He needs 50 ounces of apples for the pie. How many more pounds of apples does he need to buy?

> I draw a whole tape diagram showing the total of 50 ounces of apples that Charlie needs for the pie.

50 oz

$2\frac{1}{4}$ lb   ? lb

> I draw and label a part $2\frac{1}{4}$ pounds to show the apples Charlie bought.

> I label the remaining part that Charlie needs with a question mark, to represent what I'm trying to find out.

$2\frac{1}{4}$ lb = _____ oz

$2\frac{1}{4}$ lb = $2\frac{1}{4} \times 16$ oz

$= \frac{9}{\overset{1}{4}} \times \overset{4}{16}$ oz

$= 36$ oz

$$\begin{array}{r} {\overset{4}{\cancel{5}}} \; {\overset{10}{\cancel{0}}} \quad \text{oz} \\ - \quad 3 \quad 6 \quad \text{oz} \\ \hline 1 \quad 4 \quad \text{oz} \end{array}$$

14 oz = _____ lb

14 oz = 14×1 oz

$= 14 \times \frac{1}{16}$ lb

$= \frac{14}{16}$ lb

$= \frac{7}{8}$ lb

> I convert $2\frac{1}{4}$ pounds to ounces by multiplying by 16. $2\frac{1}{4}$ pounds is equal to 36 ounces.

> I subtract 36 ounces from the total of 50 ounces to find how many more ounces of apples Charlie needs to buy. The difference is 14 ounces.

> Since the question asks how many more **pounds** does he need to buy, I convert 14 ounces to pounds.

Charlie needs to buy $\frac{7}{8}$ pound of apples.

EUREKA MATH

©2015 Great Minds. eureka-math.org
G5-M1-HWH-1.3.0-07.2015

G5-M4-Lesson 21

Fill in the blanks.

> I think 3 times what is 18, and 5 times what is 30? The missing fraction must be $\frac{6}{6}$.

1. $\frac{3}{5} \times 1 = \frac{3}{5} \times \frac{6}{6} = \frac{18}{30}$

> I know that any number times 1, or a fraction equal to 1, will be equal to the number itself.
> $\frac{3}{5} = \frac{18}{30}$

> In order to write a fraction as a decimal, I can rename the denominator as a power of 10 (e.g., 10, 100, 1,000).
> $\frac{1}{10} = 0.1$ $\frac{1}{100} = 0.01$ $\frac{1}{1,000} = 0.001$

2. Express each fraction as an equivalent decimal.

   a. $\frac{1}{4} \times \frac{25}{25} = \frac{25}{100} = 0.25$

   > I can rename $\frac{1}{4}$ as $\frac{25}{100}$, or 0.25.

   > I look at the denominator, 4, and it is a factor of 100 and 1,000.

   > I look at the denominator, 5, and it is a factor of 10, 100, and 1,000.

   b. $\frac{4}{5} \times \frac{2}{2} = \frac{8}{10} = 0.8$

   c. $\frac{21}{20} \times \frac{5}{5} = \frac{105}{100} = 1.05$

   > Since $\frac{21}{20}$ is a fraction greater than 1, the equivalent decimal must also be greater than 1.

   d. $3\frac{21}{50} \times \frac{2}{2} = 3\frac{42}{100} = 3.42$

   > Since $3\frac{21}{50}$ is a mixed number, the equivalent decimal must be greater than 1.

   > I look at the denominator, 50, and it is a factor of 100 and 1,000.

3. Vivian has $\frac{3}{4}$ of a dollar. She buys a lollipop for 59 cents. Change both numbers into decimals, and tell how much money Vivian has after paying for the lollipop.

$$\frac{3}{4} = \frac{3}{4} \times \frac{25}{25}$$

$$= \frac{75}{100}$$

$$= 0.75$$

$59 \text{ cents} = \$0.59$

1 cent = \$0.01

$$
\begin{array}{r}
 \overset{6}{}\;\overset{15}{} \\
\$0.\;\;7\;\;\cancel{5} \\
- \;\;\$0.\;\;5\;\;9 \\
\hline
\$0.\;\;1\;\;6
\end{array}
$$

I multiply $\frac{3}{4} \times \frac{25}{25}$ to get $\frac{75}{100}$. $\frac{75}{100}$ of a dollar is equal to \$0.75.

I subtract \$0.59 from \$0.75 to find that Vivian has \$0.16 left after paying for the lollipop.

Vivian has $\$0.16$ left after paying for the lollipop.

Lesson 21:   Explain the size of the product, and relate fraction and decimal equivalence to multiplying a fraction by 1.

EUREKA MATH

©2015 Great Minds. eureka-math.org
G5-M1-HWH-1.3.0-07.2015

G5-M4-Lesson 22

1. Solve for the unknown. Rewrite each phrase as a multiplication sentence. Circle the scaling factor, and put a box around the factor naming the number of meters.

   a. $\frac{1}{2}$ as long as 8 meters = ___4___ meters

   $\left(\frac{1}{2}\right) \times \boxed{8 \text{ m}} = 4 \text{ m}$

   Half of 8 is 4, so 1 half of 8 *meters* is 4 *meters*.

   b.   8 times as long as $\frac{1}{2}$ meter = ___4___ meters

   $\left(8\right) \times \boxed{\frac{1}{2} \text{ m}} = 4 \text{ m}$

   2 times 1 half is equal to 1. So 8 times 1 half (or 8 copies of 1 half) is equal to 4.

2. Draw a tape diagram to model each situation in Problem 1, and describe what happened to the number of meters when it was multiplied by the scaling factor.

   a.

   8 m

   4 m

   This tape shows a whole of 8 meters. I partition it into 2 equal units to make halves. Half of 8 m is 4 m.

   b.

   4 m

   $\frac{1}{2}$ m

   I draw a unit of $\frac{1}{2}$ m. Then I made 8 copies of it to show $8 \times \frac{1}{2}$ m, which is equal to 4 m.

   In part (a), the scaling factor $\frac{1}{2}$ is less than 1, so the number of meters decreases.

   In part (b), the scaling factor 8 is greater than 1, so the number of meters increases.

3. Look at the inequalities in each box. Choose a single fraction to write in all three blanks that would make all three number sentences true. Explain how you know.

a.

| $\frac{3}{4} \times \frac{4}{2} > \frac{3}{4}$ | $2 \times \frac{4}{2} > 2$ | $\frac{7}{5} \times \frac{4}{2} > \frac{7}{5}$ |

Any fraction greater than 1 will work. Multiplying by a factor greater than 1, like $\frac{4}{2}$, will make the product larger than the first factor shown.

Each of these inequalities shows that the expression on the left is greater than the value on the right. Therefore, I need to think of a scaling factor that is greater than 1, like $\frac{4}{2}$.

b.

| $\frac{3}{4} \times \frac{1}{3} < \frac{3}{4}$ | $2 \times \frac{1}{3} < 2$ | $\frac{7}{5} \times \frac{1}{3} < \frac{7}{5}$ |

Any fraction less than 1 will work. Multiplying by a factor less than 1, like $\frac{1}{3}$, will make the product smaller than the first factor shown.

Each of these inequalities shows that the expression on the left is less than the value on the right. Therefore, I need to think of a scaling factor that is less than 1, like $\frac{1}{3}$.

4. A company uses a sketch to plan an advertisement on the side of a building. The lettering on the sketch is $\frac{3}{4}$ inch tall. In the actual advertisement, the letters must be 20 times as tall. How tall will the letters be on the actual advertisement?

$20 \times \frac{3}{4}$

$= \frac{20 \times 3}{4}$

$= \frac{60}{4}$

$= 15$

The letters on the sketch have been scaled down to fit on the page; therefore, the letters on the actual advertisement will be larger. In order to find out how large the actual letters will be, I multiply 20 by $\frac{3}{4}$ inch.

The letters will be 15 inches tall.

EUREKA MATH

©2015 Great Minds. eureka-math.org
G5-M1-HWH-1.3.0-07.2015

G5-M4-Lesson 23

1. Sort the following expressions by rewriting them in the table.

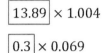 $\times 1.004$

 $\times 0.489$

102.03 $\times 4.015$

0.3 $\times 0.069$

0.72 $\times 1.24$

0.2 $\times 0.1$

> Since 0.489 is less than 1, if I multiplied it by 602, the answer would be less than 602. I'll put this expression in the column on the left.

The product is less than the boxed number:	The product is greater than the boxed number:
$\boxed{0.3} \times 0.069$ $\boxed{602} \times 0.489$ $\boxed{0.2} \times 0.1$	$\boxed{13.89} \times 1.004$ $\boxed{0.72} \times 1.24$ $\boxed{102.03} \times 4.015$

> All of the expressions in this column have a boxed number that is multiplied by a **scaling factor less than 1** (e.g., 0.069 and 0.1). Therefore, the product will be less than the boxed number.

> All of the expressions in this column have a boxed number that is multiplied by a **scaling factor more than 1** (e.g., 1.004 and 4.015). Therefore, the product will be greater than the boxed number.

2. Write a statement using one of the following phrases to compare the value of the expressions.

is slightly more than   **_is a lot more than_**   **_is slightly less than_**   **_is a lot less than_**

a. 4×0.988 _____ _is slightly less than_ _____ 4

> In this example, the product of 4×0.988 is being compared to the factor 4. Since the scaling factor, 0.988, is less than 1, the product will be less than 4. However, since the scaling factor, 0.988, is just **slightly** less than 1, the factor will also be **slightly** less than 4.

b. 1.05×0.8 _____ _is slightly more than_ _____ 0.8

c. $1,725 \times 0.013$ _____ _is a lot less than_ _____ 1,725

d. 89.001×1.3 _____ _is a lot more than_ _____ 1.3

> In this example, the product of 89.001×1.3 is being compared to the factor 1.3. Since the scaling factor, 89.001, is more than 1, the product will be more than 1.3. However, since the scaling factor, 89.001, is **a lot more** than 1, the product will also be **a lot more** than 1.3.

3. During science class, Teo, Carson, and Dhakir measure the length of their bean sprouts. Carson's sprout is 0.9 times the length of Teo's, and Dhakir's is 1.08 times the length of Teo's. Whose bean sprout is the longest? The shortest?

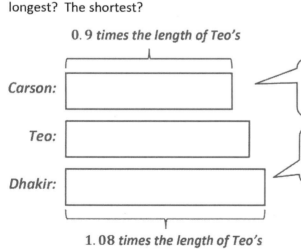

0.9 times the length of Teo's

Carson:

Teo:

Dhakir:

1.08 times the length of Teo's

> I draw a tape diagram to help me solve.

> 0.9 is less than 1, so that means Carson's sprout is shorter than Teo's.

> 1.08 is more than 1, so that means Dhakir's sprout is longer than Teo's.

Dhakir's bean sprout is the longest.

Carson's bean sprout is the shortest.

Lesson 23:   Compare the size of the product to the size of the factors.

G5-M4-Lesson 24

1. A tube contains 28 mL of medicine. If each dose is $\frac{1}{8}$ of the tube, how many milliliters is each dose?
    Express your answer as a decimal.

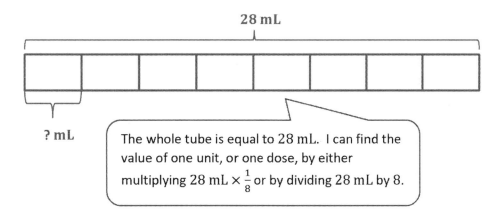

28 mL

? mL

The whole tube is equal to 28 mL. I can find the value of one unit, or one dose, by either multiplying 28 mL × $\frac{1}{8}$ or by dividing 28 mL by 8.

8 *units* = 28 mL

1 *unit* = 28 mL ÷ 8

$= \frac{28}{8}$ mL

$= 3\frac{4}{8}$ mL

$= 3\frac{1}{2}$ mL

Now I know that each dose is $3\frac{1}{2}$ mL, but the problem asks me to express my answer as a decimal. I'll need to find a fraction that is equal to $\frac{1}{2}$ and has a denominator of 10, 100, or 1,000.

I can multiply the fraction $\frac{1}{2}$ by $\frac{5}{5}$ to create an equivalent fraction with 10 as the denominator. Then I'll be able to express $3\frac{1}{2}$ as a decimal.

Each dose is $3\frac{1}{2}$ *mL.*

$3\frac{1}{2} \times \frac{5}{5} = 3\frac{5}{10} = 3.5$

Each dose is 3.5 *mL.*

Note: Some students may recognize that the fraction $\frac{1}{2}$ is equal to 0.5 without showing any work.
Encourage your child to show the amount of work that is necessary to be successful. If your child
can do basic calculations mentally, allow him or her to do so!

---

2. A clothing factory uses 1,275.2 meters of cloth a week to make shirts. How much cloth is needed to make $3\frac{3}{5}$ times as many shirts?

? m

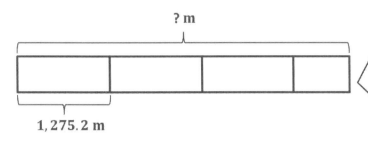

1,275.2 m

$1,275.2 \text{ m} = 1,275\frac{2}{10} \text{ m}$

I can rename 2 tenths meter as a fraction.

My tape diagram reminds me that I can use the distributive property to solve. I can multiply $1,275\frac{2}{10}$ by 3 first, to find out what 3 times as many shirts is. Then I can multiply by $\frac{3}{5}$ to find out what $\frac{3}{5}$ as many shirts is.

$$1,275\frac{2}{10} \times 3\frac{3}{5} = \left(1,275\frac{2}{10} \times 3\right) + \left(1,275\frac{2}{10} \times \frac{3}{5}\right)$$

$$= \left(3,825\frac{6}{10}\right) + \left(\frac{12,752}{10} \times \frac{3}{5}\right)$$

$$= \left(3,825\frac{6}{10}\right) + \left(\frac{12,752 \times 3}{10 \times 5}\right)$$

$$= \left(3,825\frac{6}{10}\right) + \left(\frac{38,256}{50}\right)$$

$$= \left(3,825\frac{6}{10}\right) + \left(765\frac{6}{50}\right)$$

$$= \left(3,825\frac{60}{100}\right) + \left(765\frac{12}{100}\right)$$

$$= 4,590\frac{72}{100}$$

$$= 4,590.72$$

In order to add, I make like units, or find common denominators. I'll rename each fraction using hundredths, so I can easily express my final answer as a decimal.

I can rename $\frac{72}{100}$ as 0.72 to express my final answer as a decimal.

4,590.72 meters of cloth are needed to make the shirts.

©2015 Great Minds. eureka-math.org
G5-M1-HWH-1.3.0-07.2015

3. There are $\frac{3}{4}$ as many boys as girls in a class of fifth graders. If there are 35 students in the class, how many are girls?

> I draw a tape to represent the number of girls in the class.

> I partition it into 4 equal units to make fourths.

> I can think about what my tape diagram is showing. There are a total of 7 units, and those 7 units are equal to a total of 35 students. In order to find out how many girls there are, I need to know the value of 1 unit.

Girls: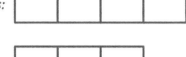

Boys:

$\}$ 35

> Since there are $\frac{3}{4}$ as many boys as girls, I draw a tape to represent the number of boys that is $\frac{3}{4}$ as long as the tape for the number of girls.

$7\ units = 35$

$1\ unit = 35 \div 7$

$1\ unit = 5$

$4\ units = 4 \times 5 = 20$

There are 20 girls in the class.

> If each unit is equal to 5 students and there are 4 units representing the girls, I can multiply to find the number of girls in the class.

G5-M4-Lesson 25

1. Draw a tape diagram and a number line to solve.

$2 \div \frac{1}{2}$

> I can think about this division expression by asking "How many halves are in 2 wholes?"

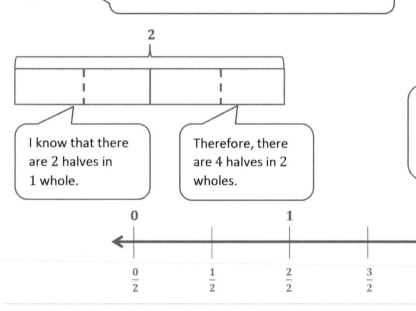

> I know that there are 2 halves in 1 whole.

> Therefore, there are 4 halves in 2 wholes.

> My number line shows the same thing. Since there are 2 halves in 1, there are 4 halves in 2.

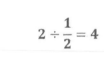
$2 \div \frac{1}{2} = 4$

$2 \div \frac{1}{2}$

> I can also think about this division expression by asking "2 is *half* of what?" or "If 2 is *half*, what is the whole?"

> I draw a unit of 2.

> And since 2 is half, I draw another unit of 2.

> My number line shows the same thing. If 2 is half, 4 is the whole.

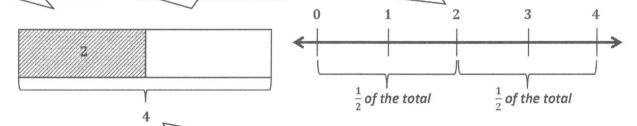

$\frac{1}{2}$ of the total $\frac{1}{2}$ of the total

> Therefore, if 2 is half, 4 is the whole!

Lesson 25:   Divide a whole number by a unit fraction.

2. Divide. Then multiply to check.

$2 \div \frac{1}{3}$

> I can think, "How many thirds are in 2?"
>
> There are 3 thirds in 1, so there are 6 thirds in 2.

> Or I can think, "If 2 is a third, what is the whole?"

$2 \div \frac{1}{3} = 6$

Check: $6 \times \frac{1}{3} = \frac{6 \times 1}{3} = \frac{6}{3} = 2$

3. A recipe for rolls calls for $\frac{1}{4}$ cup of sugar. How many batches of rolls can be made with 2 cups of sugar?

> This problem is asking me to find how many fourths are in 2.

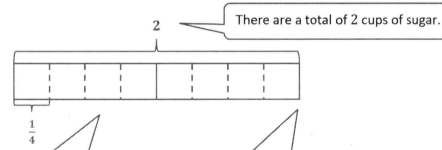

> There are a total of 2 cups of sugar.

$\frac{1}{4}$

> I partition each individual cup of sugar into 4 equal units, called fourths.

> Since there are 4 fourths in 1 cup, there are 8 fourths in 2 cups.

$2 \div \frac{1}{4} = 8$

8 batches of rolls can be made with 2 cups of sugar.

G5-M4-Lesson 26

1. Solve and support your answer with a model or tape diagram. Write your quotient in the blank.

$\frac{1}{2} \div 3 = \frac{1}{6}$

> I can think of this expression as "One half of a pan of brownies is shared equally with 3 people. How much of the pan does each person get?"

1

> I can draw a pan of brownies and shade the $\frac{1}{2}$ of a pan that will be shared.

1

> 1 half ÷ 3
>
> = 3 sixths ÷ 3
>
> = 1 sixth

> In order to share the brownies with 3 people equally, I partition it into 3 equal parts. I do the same for the other half of the pan so that I can see equal units. Each person will get $\frac{1}{6}$ of the pan of brownies.

2. Divide. Then, multiply to check.

$\frac{1}{4} \div 5$

$\frac{5}{20} \div 5 = 5 \text{ twentieths} \div 5 = 1 \text{ twentieth} = \frac{1}{20}$

> I can visualize a tape diagram. In my mind, I can see 1 fourth being partitioned into 5 equal units. Now, instead of seeing fourths, the model is showing twentieths.

> I know that 5 ÷ 5 is equal to 1.
>
> Therefore, 5 *twentieths* ÷ 5 = 1 *twentieth*, or $\frac{1}{20}$.

Check: $\frac{1}{20} \times 5 = \frac{5}{20} = \frac{1}{4}$

> I check my answer by multiplying the quotient, $\frac{1}{20}$, and the divisor, 5, to get $\frac{1}{4}$.

EUREKA MATH

Since Tim read $\frac{4}{5}$ of the book, it means he has $\frac{1}{5}$ left to read.

$$1 - \frac{4}{5} = \frac{1}{5}$$

3. Tim has read $\frac{4}{5}$ of his book. He finishes the book by reading the same amount each night for 3 nights.

a. What fraction of the book does he read on each of the 3 nights?

$$\frac{1}{5} \div 3 = \frac{3}{15} \div 3 = \frac{1}{15}$$

I can rename $\frac{1}{5}$ as $\frac{3}{15}$. Then, I divide.

3 fifteenths ÷ 3 = 1 fifteenth, or $\frac{1}{15}$.

He reads $\frac{1}{15}$ of the book on each of the 3 nights.

b. If he reads 6 pages on each of the 3 nights, how long is the book?

1 unit = 6 pages

15 units = 15 × 6 pages = 90 pages

Tim reads $\frac{1}{15}$, or 6 pages, each night.

So $\frac{1}{15}$ or 1 unit is equal to 6 pages.

The book has 90 pages.

The whole book is equal to $\frac{15}{15}$, or 15 units.

So I multiply 15 times 6.

G5-M4-Lesson 27

1. Owen ordered 2 mini cakes for a birthday party. The cakes were sliced into fifths. How many slices were there? Draw a picture to support your response.

> I draw a tape diagram and label 2 for the 2 mini cakes.

> I can think, "How many fifths are in 2?"

2

> I cut each cake into 5 equal units and get a total of 10 units.

5 fifths in 1 cake

10 fifths in 2 cakes

$2 \div \frac{1}{5} = 10$

There were 10 slices.

2. Alex has $\frac{1}{8}$ of a pizza left over. He wants to give the leftover pizza to 3 friends to share equally. What fraction of the original pizza will each friend receive? Draw a picture to support your response.

> I draw a tape diagram and label it 1 to represent the whole pizza. I cut it into 8 equal units and shade 1 unit to represent the $\frac{1}{8}$ that Alex has.

> Three friends are sharing $\frac{1}{8}$ of a pizza. I'll divide $\frac{1}{8}$ by 3 to find how much each friend will receive.

1

?

> Since the $\frac{1}{8}$ of a pizza is being shared by 3 friends, I partition the eighth into 3 equal parts. If I did that with the other $\frac{7}{8}$, that would make a total of 24 units.

$\frac{1}{8} \div 3$

$= 1 \ eighth \div 3$

$= 3 \ twenty\text{-}fourths \div 3$

$= 1 \ twenty\text{-}fourth$

Each friend will receive $\frac{1}{24}$ of a pizza.

> One eighth is equal to 3 twenty-fourths. Three twenty-fourths divided by 3 is equal to 1 twenty-fourth.

Lesson 27:   Solve problems involving fraction division.

©2015 Great Minds. eureka-math.org
G5-M1-HWH-1.3.0-07.2015

G5-M4-Lesson 28

> My story problem has to be about 4 meters of string.

1. Create and solve a division story problem about 4 meters of string that is modeled by the tape diagram below.

> The whole or dividend is 4 meters, and it is being cut into units of $\frac{1}{3}$ meter. One third is the divisor.

Allison has 4 meters of string. She cuts each meter equally into thirds. How many thirds will she have altogether?

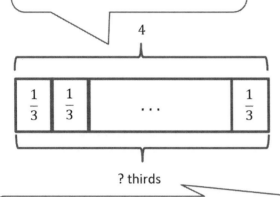

4

$$4 \div \frac{1}{3} = 12$$

Allison will have 12 thirds.

? thirds

> How many thirds are in 4? I can solve by dividing, $4 \div \frac{1}{3}$.

> Since there are 3 thirds in 1, $2 = 6$ thirds, $3 = 9$ thirds, and $4 = 12$ thirds. Therefore, 4 divided by $\frac{1}{3}$ is equal to 12.

2. Create and solve a story problem about $\frac{1}{3}$ pound of peanuts that is modeled by the tape diagram below.

> The dividend, $\frac{1}{3}$, is being divided into 4 equal parts. This model shows $\frac{1}{3} \div 4$.

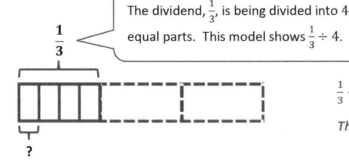

$$\frac{1}{3} \div 4 = \frac{1}{12}$$

There are $\frac{1}{12}$ pound of peanuts in each bag.

Juanita bought $\frac{1}{3}$ pound of peanuts. She splits the peanuts equally into 4 bags. How many pounds of peanuts are in each bag?

3. Draw a tape diagram and create a word problem for the following expression, and then solve.

$2 \div \frac{1}{5} = 10$

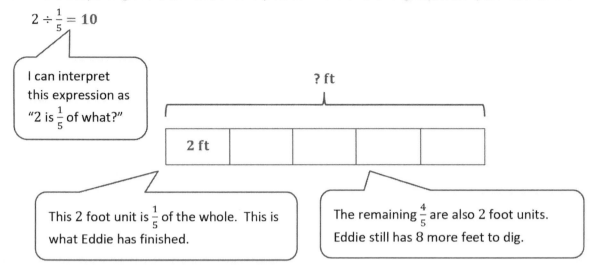

I can interpret this expression as "2 is $\frac{1}{5}$ of what?"

? ft

2 ft

This 2 foot unit is $\frac{1}{5}$ of the whole. This is what Eddie has finished.

The remaining $\frac{4}{5}$ are also 2 foot units. Eddie still has 8 more feet to dig.

After digging a tunnel 2 feet long, Eddie had finished $\frac{1}{5}$ of the tunnel. How long will the tunnel be when Eddie is done?

The tunnel will be 10 feet long.

Lesson 28:   Write equations and word problems corresponding to tape and number line diagrams.

G5-M4-Lesson 29

1. Divide. Rewrite each expression as a division sentence with a fraction divisor, and fill in the blanks.

   a. $4 \div 0.1 = 4 \div \frac{1}{10} = 40$

   There are __10__ tenths in 1 whole.

   There are __40__ tenths in 4 wholes.

   b. $3.5 \div 0.1 = 3.5 \div \frac{1}{10} = 35$

   > There are 10 tenths in 1, so there are 30 tenths in 3.

   There are __30__ tenths in 3 wholes.

   There are __5__ tenths in 5 tenths.

   There are __35__ tenths in 3.5.

   c. $5 \div 0.01 = 5 \div \frac{1}{100} = 500$

   There are __100__ hundredths in 1 whole.

   There are __500__ hundredths in 5 wholes.

   d. $2.7 \div 0.01 = 2.7 \div \frac{1}{100} = 270$

   > There are 100 hundredths in 1, so there are 200 hundredths in 2.

   There are __200__ hundredths in 2 wholes.

   There are __70__ hundredths in 7 tenths.

   > There are 10 hundredths in 1 tenth, so there are 70 hundredths in 7 tenths.

   There are __270__ hundredths in 2.7.

©2015 Great Minds. eureka-math.org
G5-M1-HWH-1.3.0-07.2015

2. Divide.

  a. $35 \div 0.1$

$$= 35 \div \frac{1}{10}$$

$$= 350$$

> I know that there are 10 tenths in 1 and 100 tenths in 10. So there are 350 tenths in 35.

  b. $1.9 \div 0.1$

$$= 1.9 \div \frac{1}{10}$$

$$= 19$$

> I can decompose 1.9 into 1 one 9 tenths. There are 10 tenths in 1, and 9 tenths in 9 tenths. Therefore, there are 19 tenths in 1.9.

  c. $3.76 \div 0.01$

$$= 3.76 \div \frac{1}{100}$$

$$= 376$$

> I can decompose 3.76 into 3 ones 7 tenths 6 hundredths. 3 ones = 300 hundredths, 7 tenths = 70 hundredths, and 6 hundredths = 6 hundredths.

Lesson 29:   Connect division by a unit fraction to division by 1 tenth and 1 hundredth.

©2015 Great Minds. eureka-math.org
G5-M1-HWH-1.3.0-07.2015

EUREKA MATH

G5-M4-Lesson 30

1. Rewrite the division expression as a fraction and divide.

a. $6.3 \div 0.9 = \dfrac{6.3}{0.9}$

> I can multiply this fraction by 1, or $\dfrac{10}{10}$, to get a denominator that is a whole number.

$= \dfrac{6.3 \times 10}{0.9 \times 10}$

$= \dfrac{63}{9}$

> After multiplying by $\dfrac{10}{10}$, the division expression is 63 divided by 9.

$= 7$

b. $6.3 \div 0.09 = \dfrac{6.3}{0.09}$

> I can multiply this fraction by 1, or $\dfrac{100}{100}$, to get a denominator that is a whole number.

$= \dfrac{6.3 \times 100}{0.09 \times 100}$

$= \dfrac{630}{9}$

$= 70$

c. $4.8 \div 1.2 = \dfrac{4.8}{1.2}$

$= \dfrac{4.8 \times 10}{1.2 \times 10}$

$= \dfrac{48}{12}$

$= 4$

d. $0.48 \div 0.12 = \dfrac{0.48}{0.12}$

$= \dfrac{0.48 \times 100}{0.12 \times 100}$

$= \dfrac{48}{12}$

$= 4$

©2015 Great Minds. eureka-math.org
G5-M1-HWH-1.3.0-07.2015

2. Mr. Huynh buys 2.4 kg of flour for his bakery.

   a. If he pours 0.8 kg of flour into separate bags, how many bags of flour can he make?

   > I can divide 2.4 kg by 0.8 kg to find the number of bags of flour he can make.

   $$2.4 \div 0.8 = \frac{2.4}{0.8}$$
   $$= \frac{2.4 \times 10}{0.8 \times 10}$$
   $$= \frac{24}{8}$$

   > 24 divided by 8 is equal to 3.

   $$= 3$$

   He can make 3 bags of flour.

   b. If he pours 0.4 kg of flour into separate bags, how many bags of flour can he make?

   $$2.4 \div 0.4 = \frac{2.4}{0.4}$$
   $$= \frac{2.4 \times 10}{0.4 \times 10}$$
   $$= \frac{24}{4}$$
   $$= 6$$

   He can make 6 bags of flour.

Lesson 30:   Divide decimal dividends by non-unit decimal divisors.

©2015 Great Minds. eureka-math.org
G5-M1-HWH-1.3.0-07.2015

G5-M4-Lesson 31

1. Estimate, and then divide.

> I can think of multiplying both the dividend (89.6) and the divisor (0.8) by 10 to get $896 \div 8$.

a. $89.6 \div 0.8 \approx 880 \div 8 = 110$

$= \dfrac{89.6}{0.8}$

> I can multiply this fraction by 1, or $\frac{10}{10}$, to get a denominator that is a whole number.

$= \dfrac{89.6 \times 10}{0.8 \times 10}$

$= \dfrac{896}{8}$

> I use the long division algorithm to solve 896 divided by 8. The answer is 112, which is very close to my estimated answer of 110.

$= 112$

```
        1  1  2
   8 |  8  9  6
     -  8
        0  9
     -     8
           1  6
     -     1  6
              0
```

> I'll imagine multiplying both the dividend and the divisor by 100 to get $524 \div 4$.

b. $5.24 \div 0.04 \approx 400 \div 4 = 100$

$= \dfrac{5.24}{0.04}$

> I can multiply this fraction by 1, or $\frac{100}{100}$, to get a denominator that is a whole number.

$= \dfrac{5.24 \times 100}{0.04 \times 100}$

$= \dfrac{524}{4}$

$= 131$

> 524 divided by 4 is equal to 131.

```
        1  3  1
   4 |  5  2  4
     -  4
        1  2
     -  1  2
           0  4
     -        4
              0
```

2. Solve using the standard algorithm. Use the thought bubble to show your thinking as you rename the divisor as a whole number.

$2.64 \div 0.06 = 44$

I write a note explaining how I can rewrite the division expression from $2.64 \div 0.06$ to $264 \div 6$. Both expressions are equivalent.

I multiplied 2.64 and 0.06 by 100 to get an equivalent division expression with whole numbers.

$2.64 \div 0.06 = \dfrac{264}{6}$

```
        4   4
   6 | 2   6   4
   -   2   4
       ‾‾‾‾‾‾‾‾
           2   4
   -       2   4
       ‾‾‾‾‾‾‾‾
               0
```

I solve by using the long division algorithm, $264 \div 6 = 44$.

G5-M4-Lesson 32

1. Circle the expression equivalent to *the sum of 5 and 2 divided by $\frac{1}{5}$.*

$$\frac{5+2}{5} \qquad 5+\left(2 \div \frac{1}{5}\right) \qquad \frac{1}{5} \div (5+2) \qquad \boxed{(5+2) \div \frac{1}{5}}$$

This expression represents the sum of 5 and 2 divided by 5.

This expression represents the sum of 5 and the quotient of 2 divided by $\frac{1}{5}$.

This expression represents $\frac{1}{5}$ divided by the sum of 5 and 2.

This expression is equivalent to the sum of 5 and 2 divided by $\frac{1}{5}$.

2. Fill in the chart by writing an equivalent numerical expression.

I can find "half" by dividing by 2 or by multiplying by $\frac{1}{2}$.

The *difference* between two numbers means I need to use subtraction to solve.

This is one possible way to write the numerical expression.

a.	Half as much as the difference between $1\frac{1}{4}$ and $\frac{5}{8}$	$\left(1\frac{1}{4} - \frac{5}{8}\right) \div 2$
b.	Add 3.9 and $\frac{5}{7}$, and then triple the sum.	$\left(3.9 + \frac{5}{7}\right) \times 3$

Add two numbers means I need to use addition.

I can triple a number by adding it 3 times or by multiplying by 3.

3. Fill in the chart by writing an equivalent expression in word form.

I see the subtraction sign, so I use the phrase, "difference between $\frac{3}{5}$ and _____."

I see the multiplication sign, so I use the phrase "product of $\frac{1}{4}$ and 2 tenths."

a.	*The difference between $\frac{3}{5}$ and the product of $\frac{1}{4}$ and 2 tenths*	$\frac{3}{5} - \left(\frac{1}{4} \times 0.2\right)$
b.	$\frac{3}{2}$ *times the sum of* 2.75 *and* $\frac{1}{8}$	$\left(2.75 + \frac{1}{8}\right) \times \frac{3}{2}$

I see the addition sign, so I use the phrase "*sum of 2.75 and $\frac{1}{8}$.*"

I see the multiplication symbol, so I say, "$\frac{3}{2}$ *times.*"

Evaluate means to "find the value of."

4. Evaluate the following the expression.

I see two multiplication signs in this expression, so I can solve for it from left to right. But since multiplication is associative, I can solve $\frac{4}{9} \times \frac{9}{4}$ first because I can see that the product is 1.

$\frac{1}{2} \times \frac{4}{9} \times \frac{9}{4}$

I put a parenthesis around $\frac{4}{9} \times \frac{9}{4}$ to show that I solve it first.

$= \frac{1}{2} \times \left(\frac{4}{9} \times \frac{9}{4}\right)$

$\frac{4}{9} \times \frac{9}{4}$ is equal to $\frac{36}{36}$, or 1.

$= \frac{1}{2} \times 1$

$= \frac{1}{2}$

$\frac{1}{2}$ of 1 is $\frac{1}{2}$.

Lesson 32: Interpret and evaluate numerical expressions including the language of scaling and fraction division.

©2015 Great Minds. eureka-math.org
G5-M1-HWH-1.3.0-07.2015

EUREKA MATH™

G5-M4-Lesson 33

I can represent this story with the expression $\frac{1}{4} \div 3$.

1. Mrs. Brady has $\frac{1}{4}$ liter of juice. She distributes it equally to 3 students in her tutoring group.

    a. How many liters of juice does each student get?

$\frac{1}{4} \div 3$

I can rename 1 fourth as 3 twelfths, so dividing by 3 is easier.

$= 1 \text{ fourth} \div 3$

$= 3 \text{ twelfths} \div 3$ 3 twelfths divided by 3 is 1 twelfth.

$= 1 \text{ twelfth}$

Each student gets $\frac{1}{12}$ liter of juice.

    b. How many more liters of juice will Mrs. Brady need if she wants to give each of the 36 students in her class the same amount of juice found in Part (a)?

$36 \times \frac{1}{12} \text{ liter}$

I can multiply to find how much juice she'll need to serve 36 students.

$= \frac{36 \times 1}{12} \text{ liters}$

$= \frac{36}{12} \text{ liters}$ Mrs. Brady will need 3 liters of juice for 36 students.

$= 3 \text{ liters}$

$3 \text{ liters} - \frac{1}{4} \text{ liter} = 2\frac{3}{4} \text{ liters}$ I subtract to find out how much more juice she'll need.

Mrs. Brady will need an additional $2\frac{3}{4}$ liters of juice.

EUREKA MATH   **Lesson 33:**   Create story contexts for numerical expressions and tape diagrams, and solve word problems.   57

©2015 Great Minds. eureka-math.org
G5-M1-HWH-1.3.0-07.2015

2. Austin buys $16.20 worth of grapefruit. Each grapefruit costs $0.60.

   a.   How many grapefruits does Austin buy?

> To find how many grapefruits Austin buys, I use the total cost divided by the cost of each grapefruit.

$$\$16.20 \div \$0.60$$

$$= \frac{16.2}{0.6} \times \frac{10}{10}$$

> I multiply the fraction by 1, or $\frac{10}{10}$, to get a denominator that is a whole number.

$$= \frac{162}{6}$$

$$= 27$$

```
      2  7
   ┌─────────
 6 │ 1  6  2
   − 1  2
   ──────────
         4  2
       − 4  2
   ──────────
            0
```

> I use the long division algorithm to solve 162 divided by 6. The answer is 27.

Austin buys 27 grapefruits.

   b.   At the same store, Mandy spends one third as much money on grapefruit as Austin. How many grapefruits does she buy?

> Since Mandy spent $\frac{1}{3}$ as much money on grapefruit as Austin, that means she's buying $\frac{1}{3}$ the number of grapefruit.

$$27 \div 3 = 9$$

Mandy buys 9 grapefruits.

> To find one third of a number, I can multiply by $\frac{1}{3}$ or divide by 3.

Lesson 33:   Create story contexts for numerical expressions and tape diagrams, and solve word problems.

EUREKA MATH

Homework Helpers

Grade 5
Module 5

G5-M5-Lesson 1

1. The following solids are made up of 1 cm cubes. Find the total volume of each figure, and write it in the chart below.

a.

b.

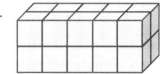

I see there are 3 cubes on the bottom and 1 cube on top. Therefore, this solid has a total of 4 cubes.

I see there are 2 layers of cubes like layers of a cake (top and bottom). There are 10 cubes on the top, and there must be 10 cubes on the bottom. Therefore, this solid has a total of 20 cubes.

Since Figure (a) is made of a total of 4 cubes, I can say that it has a volume of 4 cubic centimeters.

Figure	Volume	Explanation
a	4 cm^3	*I added* 3 *cubes and* 1 *cube.* $3 + 1 = 4$
b	20 cm^3	*I counted the top layer and then multiplied by* 2.

2. Draw a figure with the given volume on the dot paper.

a.   2 cubic units

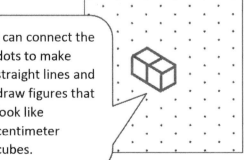

I can connect the dots to make straight lines and draw figures that look like centimeter cubes.

b.   4 cubic units

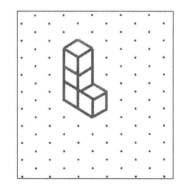

3. Allison says that the figure below, made of 1 cm cubes, has a volume of 4 cubic centimeters.

   a. Explain her mistake.

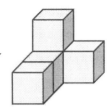

   Allison is not counting the cube that is hidden. The cube that is on the
   second layer needs to be sitting on a hidden cube. The volume of this
   figure is 5 cubic centimeters.

   > I see there are 4 cubes showing, but there
   > is one hidden under the 1 cube on top.

   b. Imagine if Allison adds to the second layer so the cubes completely cover the first layer in the figure
       above. What would be the volume of the new structure? Explain how you know.

   The volume would be 8 cm^3. *I counted the first layer, and then multiplied by 2.*

   $$4 \text{ cm}^3 \times 2 = 8 \text{ cm}^3$$

   > Since Allison wants to build a second layer that is the
   > same as the first layer, I can just multiply 4 cubes times 2.

©2015 Great Minds. eureka-math.org
G5-M1-HWH-1.3.0-07.2015

G5-M5-Lesson 2

1. Shade the following figures on centimeter grid paper. Cut and fold each to make 3 open boxes, taping them so they hold their shapes. Pack each box with cubes. Write how many cubes fill the box.

a.

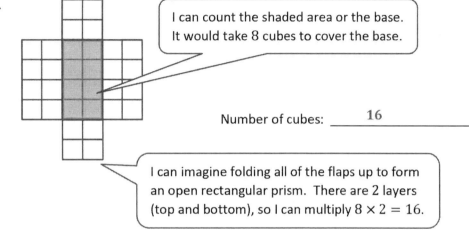

I can count the shaded area or the base. It would take 8 cubes to cover the base.

Number of cubes: _____16_____

I can imagine folding all of the flaps up to form an open rectangular prism. There are 2 layers (top and bottom), so I can multiply $8 \times 2 = 16$.

b.

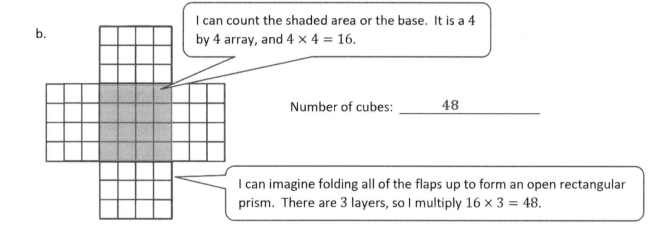

I can count the shaded area or the base. It is a 4 by 4 array, and $4 \times 4 = 16$.

Number of cubes: _____48_____

I can imagine folding all of the flaps up to form an open rectangular prism. There are 3 layers, so I multiply $16 \times 3 = 48$.

EUREKA
MATH™   Lesson 2:   Find the volume of a right rectangular prism by packing with cubic units   3
                             and counting.

©2015 Great Minds. eureka-math.org
G5-M1-HWH-1.3.0-07.2015

2. How many centimeter cubes would fit in each box? Explain your answer using words and diagrams on the box. (The figures are not drawn to scale.)

a.

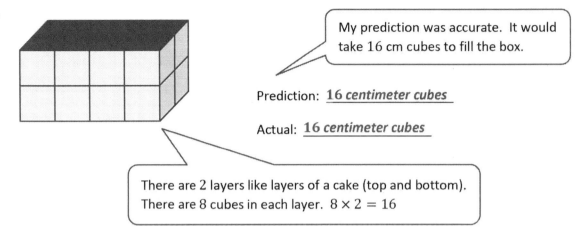

My prediction was accurate. It would take 16 cm cubes to fill the box.

Prediction: <u>16 *centimeter cubes*</u>

Actual: <u>16 *centimeter cubes*</u>

There are 2 layers like layers of a cake (top and bottom). There are 8 cubes in each layer. $8 \times 2 = 16$

There are 2 layers: top and bottom. Each layer has 8 cubes, and 8 cubes $\times$ 2 = 16 cubes.

b.

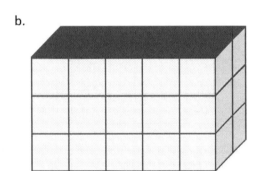

This box looks like it might hold twice as many cubes as the first one, so my prediction is 32 cubes.

Prediction: <u>32 *centimeter cubes*</u>

Actual: <u>30 *centimeter cubes*</u>

There are 3 layers: top, middle, and bottom.

Each layer has 10 cubes, and 10 cubes $\times$ 3 = 30 cubes.

Lesson 2:   Find the volume of a right rectangular prism by packing with cubic units and counting.   **EUREKA MATH**

©2015 Great Minds. eureka-math.org
G5-M1-HWH-1.3.0-07.2015

G5-M5-Lesson 3

1. Use the prisms to find the volume.
    - Build the rectangular prism pictured below to the left with your cubes, if necessary.
    - Decompose it into layers in three different ways, and show your thinking on the blank prisms.
    - Complete the missing information in the table.

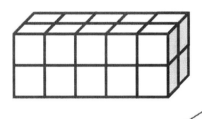

Number of Layers	Number of Cubes in Each Layer	Volume of the Prism
2	10	20 cubic cm
5	4	20 cubic cm
2	10	20 cubic cm

> I can look at the rectangular prism above or the ones I cut below to help me record the information in the table.

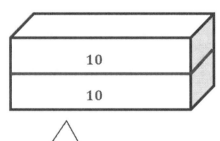

> I will cut it horizontally (top and bottom like layers in a cake). I have 2 layers, and there are 10 cubes in each layer.

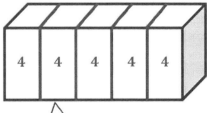

> I will cut it vertically (left to right like slices of bread). I have 5 layers, and there are 4 cubes in each layer.

> I will cut it into 2 layers, front and back. There are 10 cubes in each layer.

I can visualize a prism that is 5 in × 5 in × 1 in. When looking at the prism from the top, it would look like a square since the length and the width are equal. The prism is also just one inch tall, so it looks like the bottom layer of a cake.

2. Joseph makes a rectangular prism 5 inches by 5 inches by 1 inch. He then decides to create layers equal to his first one. Fill in the chart below, and explain how you know the volume of each new prism.

To find the volume in 3 layers, I will multiply 3 times 25 in^3. The answer is 75 in^3.

Number of Layers	Volume	Explanation
3	75 in^3	1 *layer*: 25 in^3 3 *layers*: 3×25 in$^3 = 75$ in^3
5	125 in^3	1 *layer*: 25 in^3 5 *layers*: 5×25 in$^3 = 125$ in^3

To find the volume of 5 layers, I will multiply 5 times 25 in^3. The answer is 125 in^3.

©2015 Great Minds. eureka-math.org
G5-M1-HWH-1.3.0-07.2015

G5-M5-Lesson 4

1. Each rectangular prism is built from centimeter cubes. State the dimensions, and find the volume.

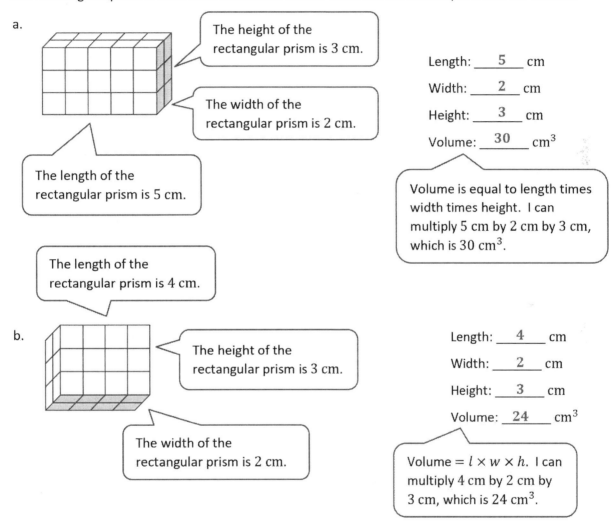

a.

The height of the rectangular prism is 3 cm.

The width of the rectangular prism is 2 cm.

The length of the rectangular prism is 5 cm.

Length: _____5_____ cm

Width: _____2_____ cm

Height: _____3_____ cm

Volume: _____30_____ cm^3

Volume is equal to length times width times height. I can multiply 5 cm by 2 cm by 3 cm, which is 30 cm^3.

The length of the rectangular prism is 4 cm.

b.

The height of the rectangular prism is 3 cm.

The width of the rectangular prism is 2 cm.

Length: _____4_____ cm

Width: _____2_____ cm

Height: _____3_____ cm

Volume: _____24_____ cm^3

Volume $= l \times w \times h$. I can multiply 4 cm by 2 cm by 3 cm, which is 24 cm^3.

2. Write a multiplication sentence that you could use to calculate the volume for each rectangular prism in Problem 1. Include the units in your sentences.

   a. $5 \text{ cm} \times 2 \text{ cm} \times 3 \text{ cm} = 30 \text{ cm}^3$

   b. $4 \text{ cm} \times 2 \text{ cm} \times 3 \text{ cm} = 24 \text{ cm}^3$

3. Calculate the volume of each rectangular prism. Include the units in your number sentences.

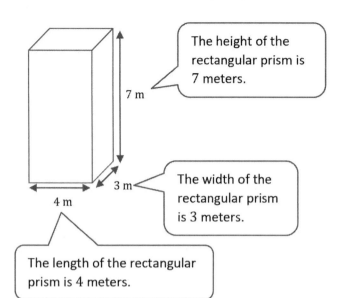

The height of the rectangular prism is 7 meters.

7 m

3 m

The width of the rectangular prism is 3 meters.

4 m

The length of the rectangular prism is 4 meters.

$V = \underline{\quad 4\text{ m} \times 3\text{ m} \times 7\text{ m} = 84\text{ m}^3 \quad}$

I multiply the 3 dimensions together to find the volume.

4. Meilin is constructing a box in the shape of a rectangular prism to store her small toys. It has a length of 10 inches, a width of 5 inches, and a height of 7 inches. What is the volume of the box?

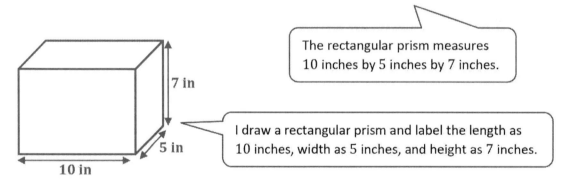

The rectangular prism measures 10 inches by 5 inches by 7 inches.

7 in

5 in

10 in

I draw a rectangular prism and label the length as 10 inches, width as 5 inches, and height as 7 inches.

Volume = length × width × height

$V = 10\text{ in} \times 5\text{ in} \times 7\text{ in} = 350\text{ in}^3$

The volume of the box is 350 cubic inches.

©2015 Great Minds. eureka-math.org
G5-M1-HWH-1.3.0-07.2015

G5-M5-Lesson 5

1. Kevin filled a container with 40 centimeter cubes. Shade the beaker to show how much water the container will hold. Explain how you know.

   It will hold 40 *milliliters of water. I know that* $1 \text{ cm}^3 = 1 \text{ mL}$.
   Therefore, 40 cm^3 *is equal to* 40 mL.

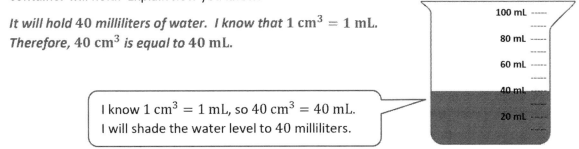

   I know $1 \text{ cm}^3 = 1 \text{ mL}$, so $40 \text{ cm}^3 = 40 \text{ mL}$.
   I will shade the water level to 40 milliliters.

2. A beaker contains 200 mL of water. Joe wants to pour the water into a container that will hold the water. Which of the containers pictured below could he use? Explain your choices.

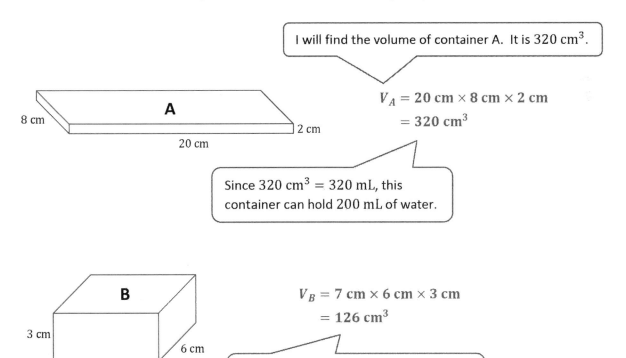

   I will find the volume of container A. It is 320 cm^3.

   $$V_A = 20 \text{ cm} \times 8 \text{ cm} \times 2 \text{ cm}$$
   $$= 320 \text{ cm}^3$$

   Since $320 \text{ cm}^3 = 320 \text{ mL}$, this container can hold 200 mL of water.

   $$V_B = 7 \text{ cm} \times 6 \text{ cm} \times 3 \text{ cm}$$
   $$= 126 \text{ cm}^3$$

   Since $126 \text{ cm}^3 = 126 \text{ mL}$, this container cannot hold 200 mL of water.

I can find the volume of container C by multiplying the area of the front face by the width.

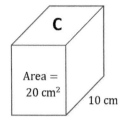

$V_C = 20 \text{ cm}^2 \times 10 \text{ cm}$

$\quad = 200 \text{ cm}^3$

Since $200 \text{ cm}^3 = 200 \text{ mL}$, this container can hold 200 mL of water.

I can find the volume of container D by multiplying the area of the top face by the height.

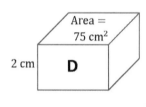

$V_D = 75 \text{ cm}^2 \times 2 \text{ cm}$

$\quad = 150 \text{ cm}^3$

Since $150 \text{ cm}^3 = 150 \text{ mL}$, this container will not be able to hold 200 mL of water.

Joe will be able to use container A because the volume is 320 cm^3. *He will also be able to use container C because the volume is* 200 cm^3. *He will not be able to use containers B and D because they are too small.*

©2015 Great Minds. eureka-math.org
G5-M1-HWH-1.3.0-07.2015

G5-M5-Lesson 6

1. Find the total volume of the figures, and record your solution strategy.

   a.

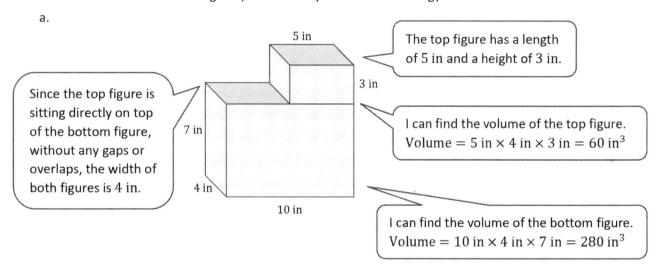

The top figure has a length of 5 in and a height of 3 in.

Since the top figure is sitting directly on top of the bottom figure, without any gaps or overlaps, the width of both figures is 4 in.

I can find the volume of the top figure. Volume = 5 in × 4 in × 3 in = 60 in^3

I can find the volume of the bottom figure. Volume = 10 in × 4 in × 7 in = 280 in^3

Volume: _____ 340 in^3 _____

I will add both figures' volumes together. 60 in^3 + 280 in^3 = 340 in^3

Solution Strategy:

I found the top figure's volume, 60 in^3, and the bottom figure's volume, 280 in^3. Then, I added both volumes together to get a total of 340 in^3.

EUREKA MATH™

Lesson 6:   Find the total volume of solid figures composed of two non-overlapping rectangular prisms.

©2015 Great Minds. eureka-math.org
G5-M1-HWH-1.3.0-07.2015

11

b.

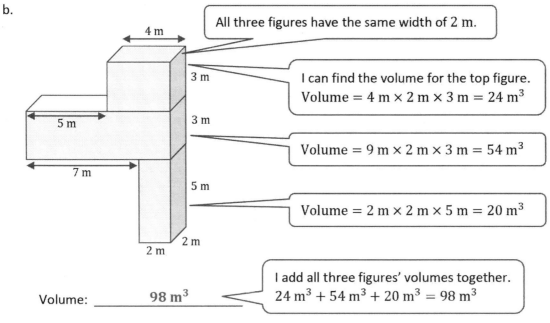

All three figures have the same width of 2 m.

I can find the volume for the top figure.
Volume = 4 m × 2 m × 3 m = 24 m³

Volume = 9 m × 2 m × 3 m = 54 m³

Volume = 2 m × 2 m × 5 m = 20 m³

Volume: _____ 98 m³

I add all three figures' volumes together.
24 m³ + 54 m³ + 20 m³ = 98 m³

Solution Strategy:

I found the top figure's volume, 24 m³, the middle figure's volume, 54 m³, and the bottom figure's volume, 20 m³. Then, I added all three volumes together to get a total of 98 m³.

2. A fish tank has a base area of 65 cm² and is filled with water to a depth of 21 cm. If the height of the tank is 30 cm, how much more water will be needed to fill the tank to the brim?

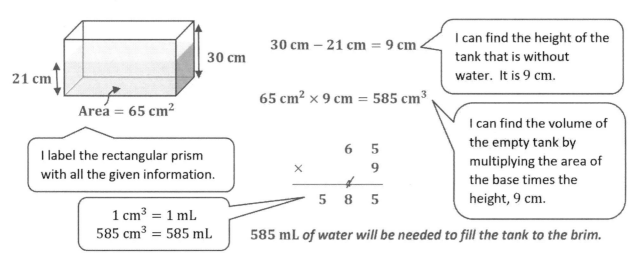

30 cm − 21 cm = 9 cm

I can find the height of the tank that is without water. It is 9 cm.

65 cm² × 9 cm = 585 cm³

I can find the volume of the empty tank by multiplying the area of the base times the height, 9 cm.

I label the rectangular prism with all the given information.

$$
\begin{array}{r}
6\;5 \\
\times\quad\;\;9 \\
\hline
5\;8\;5
\end{array}
$$

1 cm³ = 1 mL
585 cm³ = 585 mL

585 mL of water will be needed to fill the tank to the brim.

EUREKA
MATH™

©2015 Great Minds. eureka-math.org
G5-M1-HWH-1.3.0-07.2015

G5-M5-Lesson 7

Edwin builds rectangular planters.

1. Edwin's first planter is 6 feet long and 2 feet wide. The container is filled with soil to a height of 3 feet in the planter. What is the volume of soil in the planter? Explain your work using a diagram.

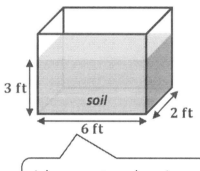

$$\text{Volume} = \text{length} \times \text{width} \times \text{height}$$
$$V = 6\,\text{ft} \times 2\,\text{ft} \times 3\,\text{ft} = 36\,\text{ft}^3$$

The volume of soil in the planter is 36 cubic feet.

I draw a rectangular prism and label all the given information.

I can multiply the length, width, and height of the soil to find the volume of the soil in the planter.

In order to have a volume of 50 cubic feet, I have to think of different factors that I can multiply to get 50. Since volume is three-dimensional, I will have to think of 3 factors.

2. Edwin wants to grow some flowers in two planters. He wants each planter to have a volume of 50 cubic feet, but he wants them to have different dimensions. Show two different ways Edwin can make these planters, and draw diagrams with the planters' measurements on them.

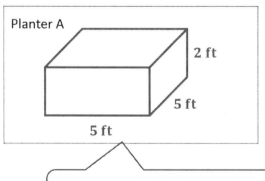

I need to think of 3 factors that give a product of 50.

$$\text{Volume} = l \times w \times h$$
$$V = 5\,\text{ft} \times 5\,\text{ft} \times 2\,\text{ft} = 50\,\text{ft}^3$$

I draw a rectangular prism and label it as 5 feet by 5 feet by 2 feet.

I can verify my answer by finding the volume for Planter A. The answer is 50 cubic feet.

EUREKA MATH   **Lesson 7:**   Solve word problems involving the volume of rectangular prisms with whole number edge lengths.   **13**

©2015 Great Minds. eureka-math.org
G5-M1-HWH-1.3.0-07.2015

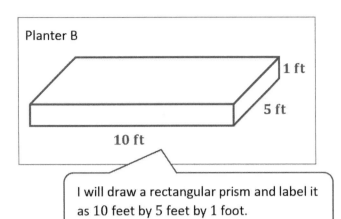

Planter B

1 ft

5 ft

10 ft

I need the 3 different factors for Planter B.
$10 \times 5 \times 1 = 50$

Volume $= l \times w \times h$
$V = 10$ ft $\times 5$ ft $\times 1$ ft $= 50$ ft^3

I will draw a rectangular prism and label it as 10 feet by 5 feet by 1 foot.

In order to have a volume of 30 cubic feet, I have to think of three factors that give a product of 30.

3. Edwin wants to make one planter that extends from the ground to just below his back window. The window starts 3 feet off the ground. If he wants the planter to hold 30 cubic feet of soil, name one way he could build the planter so it is not taller than 3 feet. Explain how you know.

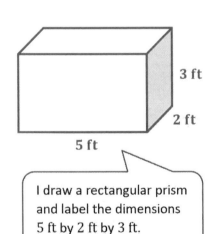

3 ft

2 ft

5 ft

The volume is 30 cubic feet, and one of the dimensions must not be more than 3 feet. So, I will keep the height as 3 feet.

I already know the volume is 30 ft^3, and the height is 3 ft, so I'll divide the volume by the height to find the area of the base.

30 ft$^3 \div 3$ ft $= 10$ ft^2

I draw a rectangular prism and label the dimensions 5 ft by 2 ft by 3 ft.

10 ft$^2 = 5$ ft $\times 2$ ft

Length $= 5$ ft

Width $= 2$ ft

Height $= 3$ ft

Now that I know the area of the base of the planter is 10 ft^2, I need to think of two factors that have a product of 10. 5 and 2 will work!

Since Edwin wants to build a planter with a height of 3 ft and a volume of 30 ft^3, the base of the planter should have an area of 10 ft^2. I drew a planter with a length of 5 ft, width of 2 ft, and height of 3 ft.

14   Lesson 7:   Solve word problems involving the volume of rectangular prisms with
                            whole number edge lengths.

                    ©2015 Great Minds. eureka-math.org
                    G5-M1-HWH-1.3.0-07.2015

EUREKA
MATH

G5-M5-Lesson 8

1. I have a prism with the dimensions of 8 in by 12 in by 20 in. Calculate the volume of the prism, and then give the dimensions of two different prisms that each have $\frac{1}{4}$ of the volume.

> To find $\frac{1}{4}$ of the volume, I can use the original prism's volume divided by 4.
> $\frac{1}{4}$ of 1,920 in^3 is equal to 480 in^3.

	Length	Width	Height	Volume
Original Prism	8 in.	12 in.	20 in.	1,920 in^3

> I multiply the three dimensions to find the original volume.
> 8 in × 12 in × 20 in = 1,920 in^3

	Length	Width	Height	Volume
Prism 1	2 in.	12 in.	20 in.	480 in^3

> In order to create a volume that is $\frac{1}{4}$ of 1,920, I can change one of the dimensions and keep the others the same.
> $\frac{1}{4}$ of 8 in = 2 in

> 2 in × 12 in × 20 in = 480 in^3

	Length	Width	Height	Volume
Prism 2	8 in.	6 in.	10 in.	480 in^3

> Another way I can create a volume that is $\frac{1}{4}$ of 1,920 is to change two of the dimensions and keep the other the same.
> $\frac{1}{2}$ of 12 in = 6 in
> $\frac{1}{2}$ of 20 in = 10 in

EUREKA MATH   **Lesson 8:**   Apply concepts and formulas of volume to design a sculpture using rectangular prisms within given parameters.   **15**

©2015 Great Minds. eureka-math.org
G5-M1-HWH-1.3.0-07.2015

Kayla's bedroom has a volume of 800 ft³.
$10 \text{ ft} \times 8 \text{ ft} \times 10 \text{ ft} = 800 \text{ ft}^3$

One way to double the volume is to double one dimension and keep the others the same.

2. Kayla's bedroom has the dimensions of 10 ft by 8 ft by 10 ft. Her den has the same height (10 ft) but double the volume. Give two sets of the possible dimensions of the den and the volume of the den.

Length: $10 \text{ ft} \times 2 = 20 \text{ ft}$

I can double the length, $10 \text{ ft} \times 2 = 20 \text{ ft}$, and keep both the width and the height the same.

Width: 8 ft

Height: 10 ft

Volume $= 20 \text{ ft} \times 8 \text{ ft} \times 10 \text{ ft} = 1,600 \text{ ft}^3$

1,600 ft³ is double the original volume of 800 ft³.

Length: $10 \text{ ft} \times 4 = 40 \text{ ft}$

In order to double the volume, I can also quadruple the length and cut the width in half.

Width: $8 \text{ ft} \times \frac{1}{2} = 4 \text{ ft}$

Height: 10 ft

Volume $= 40 \text{ ft} \times 4 \text{ ft} \times 10 \text{ ft} = 1,600 \text{ ft}^3$

1,600 ft³ is double the original volume of 800 ft³.

Lesson 8:   Apply concepts and formulas of volume to design a sculpture using rectangular prisms within given parameters.

EUREKA MATH

©2015 Great Minds. eureka-math.org
G5-M1-HWH-1.3.0-07.2015

G5-M5-Lesson 9

Find three rectangular prisms around your house. Describe the item you are measuring (e.g., cereal box, tissue box), and then measure each dimension to the nearest whole inch and calculate the volume.

a. Rectangular Prism A

Item: *Cereal box*

I will measure a cereal box, and then multiply the three dimensions to find the volume.

Height: _____12_____ inches

Length: _____8_____ inches

Width: _____3_____ inches

Volume: _____288_____ cubic inches

Volume = length × width × height
= 8 in × 3 in × 12 in
= 288 in^3

b. Rectangular Prism B

Item: Tissue box

I will measure a tissue box, and then multiply the three dimensions to find the volume.

Height: _____3_____ inches

Length: _____9_____ inches

Width: _____5_____ inches

Volume: _____135_____ cubic inches

Volume = length × width × height
= 9 in × 5 in × 3 in
= 45 in^2 × 3 in
= 135 in^3

The volume of the tissue box is 135 cubic inches.

EUREKA MATH   Lesson 9:   Apply concepts and formulas of volume to design a sculpture using rectangular prisms within given parameters.   17

©2015 Great Minds. eureka-math.org
G5-M1-HWH-1.3.0-07.2015

G5-M5-Lesson 10

1. Alex tiled some rectangles using square units. Sketch the rectangles if necessary. Fill in the missing information, and then confirm the area by multiplying.

Rectangle A:

> I look at Rectangle A's dimensions, 4 units by $2\frac{1}{2}$ units.

Rectangle A is

4 units long by $2\frac{1}{2}$ unit wide.

Area = ___10___ square units

4 *units*

> I can draw a length of 4 units.

> I can draw a rectangle and show a width of $2\frac{1}{2}$ units.

2 *units*

$\frac{1}{2}$ ***unit***

> I can count the halves and see that there are 4 half square units, which is the same as 2 square units. I can multiply too.
> 4 units $\times \frac{1}{2}$ unit = 2 square units

> I can count the squares and see that there are 8 whole square units. I can multiply too.
> 4 units $\times$ 2 units = 8 square units

> 8 square units + 2 square units = 10 square units

4 *units* $\times 2\frac{1}{2}$ *units*

> I can confirm the area by multiplying the length and width.

$(4 \times 2) + \left(4 \times \frac{1}{2}\right)$

> The area of Rectangle A is 10 square units.

> I can use the rectangle I drew and the distributive property to help me multiply.
> 4 units $\times$ 2 units = 8 square units
> 4 units $\times \frac{1}{2}$ unit = $\frac{4}{2}$ square units = 2 square units

$= 8 + \frac{4}{2}$

$= 8 + 2$

$= 10$

Lesson 10:   Find the area of rectangles with whole-by-mixed and whole-by-fractional number side lengths by tiling, record by drawing, and relate to fraction multiplication.

EUREKA MATH

2. Juanita made a mosaic from different colored rectangular tiles. Two blue tiles measured $2\frac{1}{2}$ inches $\times$ 3 inches. Five white tiles measured 3 inches $\times 2\frac{1}{4}$ inches. What is the area of the whole mosaic in square inches?

I can find the area of one blue tile.

$2\frac{1}{2}$ in $\times$ 3 in

$(2 \times 3) + \left(\frac{1}{2} \times 3\right)$

$= 6 + \frac{3}{2}$

$= 6 + 1\frac{1}{2}$

$= 7\frac{1}{2}$

The area of 1 blue tile is $7\frac{1}{2}$ in^2.

To find the area of the two blue tiles, I can multiply the area by 2.

$1\ unit = 7\frac{1}{2}\ \text{in}^2$

$2\ units = 2 \times 7\frac{1}{2}\ \text{in}^2$

$= (2 \times 7) + \left(2 \times \frac{1}{2}\right)$

$= 14 + \frac{2}{2}$

$= 14 + 1$

$= 15$

The area of 2 blue tiles is 15 in^2.

I can find the area of one white tile.

3 in $\times 2\frac{1}{4}$ in

$(3 \times 2) + \left(3 \times \frac{1}{4}\right)$

$= 6 + \frac{3}{4}$

$= 6\frac{3}{4}$

The area of 1 white tile is $6\frac{3}{4}$ in^2.

To find the area of five white tiles, I can multiply the area by 5.

$1\ unit = 6\frac{3}{4}\ \text{in}^2$

$5\ units = 5 \times 6\frac{3}{4}\ \text{in}^2$

$= (5 \times 6) + \left(5 \times \frac{3}{4}\right)$

$= 30 + \frac{15}{4}$

$= 30 + 3\frac{3}{4}$

$= 33\frac{3}{4}$

The area of 5 white tiles is $33\frac{3}{4}$ in^2.

$33\frac{3}{4}$ in^2 + 15 in^2 = $48\frac{3}{4}$ in^2

I can add the two areas together to find the area of the entire mosaic.

The area of the whole mosaic is $48\frac{3}{4}$ square inches.

EUREKA MATH

Lesson 10: Find the area of rectangles with whole-by-mixed and whole-by-fractional number side lengths by tiling, record by drawing, and relate to fraction multiplication.

19

©2015 Great Minds. eureka-math.org
G5-M1-HWH-1.3.0-07.2015

G5-M5-Lesson 11

1. Cindy tiled the following rectangles using square units. Sketch the rectangles, and find the areas. Then, confirm the area by multiplying.

   a. **Rectangle A:**

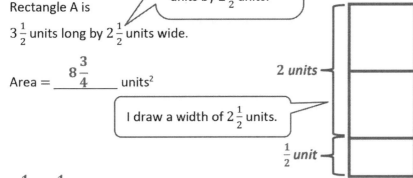

I look at Rectangle A's dimensions, $3\frac{1}{2}$ units by $2\frac{1}{2}$ units.

Rectangle A is $3\frac{1}{2}$ units long by $2\frac{1}{2}$ units wide.

Area = $8\frac{3}{4}$ units²

I draw a width of $2\frac{1}{2}$ units.

I can draw a length of $3\frac{1}{2}$ units.

3 units $\frac{1}{2}$ unit

2 units

$\frac{1}{2}$ unit

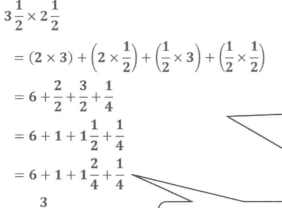

$$3\frac{1}{2} \times 2\frac{1}{2}$$

$$= (2 \times 3) + \left(2 \times \frac{1}{2}\right) + \left(\frac{1}{2} \times 3\right) + \left(\frac{1}{2} \times \frac{1}{2}\right)$$

$$= 6 + \frac{2}{2} + \frac{3}{2} + \frac{1}{4}$$

$$= 6 + 1 + 1\frac{1}{2} + \frac{1}{4}$$

$$= 6 + 1 + 1\frac{2}{4} + \frac{1}{4}$$

$$= 8\frac{3}{4}$$

I can look at the rectangle above to help me multiply.
2 units × 3 units = 6 units²
2 units × $\frac{1}{2}$ unit = $\frac{2}{2}$ unit² = 1 unit²
$\frac{1}{2}$ unit × 3 units = $\frac{3}{2}$ units² = $1\frac{1}{2}$ units²
$\frac{1}{2}$ unit × $\frac{1}{2}$ unit = $\frac{1}{4}$ unit²

I rename $1\frac{1}{2}$ as $1\frac{2}{4}$ so I can add.

The area of Rectangle A is $8\frac{3}{4}$ square units.

Lesson 11:   Find the area of rectangles with mixed-by-mixed and fraction-by-fraction side lengths by tiling, record by drawing, and relate to fraction multiplication.

EUREKA
MATH™

©2015 Great Minds. eureka-math.org
G5-M1-HWH-1.3.0-07.2015

b. **Rectangle B:**

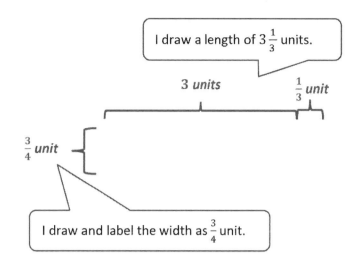

Rectangle B is

$3\frac{1}{3}$ units long by $\frac{3}{4}$ unit wide.

Area = ___$2\frac{1}{2}$___ units²

> I can multiply to find the area.

> I draw a length of $3\frac{1}{3}$ units.

> 3 *units* $\frac{1}{3}$ *unit*

> $\frac{3}{4}$ *unit*

> I draw and label the width as $\frac{3}{4}$ unit.

$3\frac{1}{3} \times \frac{3}{4}$

$= \left(\frac{3}{4} \times 3\right) + \left(\frac{3}{4} \times \frac{1}{3}\right)$

$= \frac{9}{4} + \frac{3}{12}$

$= 2\frac{1}{4} + \frac{1}{4}$

$= 2\frac{2}{4}$

$= 2\frac{1}{2}$

> I can look at the rectangle above to help me multiply.
> $\frac{3}{4}$ unit × 3 units $= \frac{9}{4}$ unit² $= 2\frac{1}{4}$ unit²
> $\frac{3}{4}$ unit × $\frac{1}{3}$ unit $= \frac{3}{12}$ unit² $= \frac{1}{4}$ unit²

> The area of Rectangle B is $2\frac{1}{2}$ square units.

EUREKA MATH   Lesson 11:   Find the area of rectangles with mixed-by-mixed and fraction-by-fraction side lengths by tiling, record by drawing, and relate to fraction multiplication.   21

©2015 Great Minds. eureka-math.org
G5-M1-HWH-1.3.0-07.2015

2. A square has a perimeter of 36 inches. What is the area of the square?

All four sides are equal in a square.

Since the perimeter of the square is 36 inches, I will use 36 inches divided by 4 to find the length of one side. 36 inches ÷ 4 = 9 inches

?

Area = ?

Perimeter = 36 in

36 in ÷ 4 = 9 in

Area is equal to length times width. I will multiply 9 inches times 9 inches to find an area of 81 square inches.

Area = length × width

     = 9 in × 9 in

     = 81 in^2

I can draw a square and label both the area and the side length with a question mark.

The area of the square is 81 in^2.

Lesson 11:   Find the area of rectangles with mixed-by-mixed and fraction-by-fraction side lengths by tiling, record by drawing, and relate to fraction multiplication.

©2015 Great Minds. eureka-math.org
G5-M1-HWH-1.3.0-07.2015

EUREKA
MATH

G5-M5-Lesson 12

1. Measure the rectangle to the nearest $\frac{1}{4}$ inch with your ruler, and label the dimensions. Use the area model to find the area.

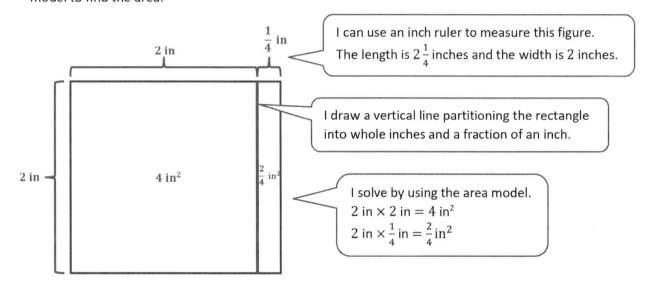

I can use an inch ruler to measure this figure. The length is $2\frac{1}{4}$ inches and the width is 2 inches.

I draw a vertical line partitioning the rectangle into whole inches and a fraction of an inch.

I solve by using the area model.
2 in × 2 in = 4 in²
2 in × $\frac{1}{4}$ in = $\frac{2}{4}$ in²

$4 \text{ in}^2 + \frac{2}{4} \text{ in}^2$

I add the two partial areas together to find the total area.

$= 4 \text{ in}^2 + \frac{1}{2} \text{ in}^2$

$= 4\frac{1}{2} \text{ in}^2$

$\text{Area} = 4\frac{1}{2} \text{ in}^2$

2. Find the area of rectangle with the following dimensions. Explain your thinking using the area model.

$2\frac{3}{4}$ ft $\times 1\frac{3}{4}$ ft

> The length is $2\frac{3}{4}$ feet, and the width is $1\frac{3}{4}$ feet.

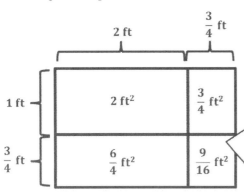

> I partition my area model into whole foot parts and fraction of a foot parts.

> I mutliply to find the four partial areas.
>
> 1 ft $\times$ 2 ft = 2 ft^2
>
> 1 ft $\times \frac{3}{4}$ ft = $\frac{3}{4}$ ft^2
>
> $\frac{3}{4}$ ft $\times$ 2 ft = $\frac{6}{4}$ ft^2
>
> $\frac{3}{4}$ ft $\times \frac{3}{4}$ ft = $\frac{9}{16}$ ft^2

$2 + \dfrac{3}{4} + \dfrac{6}{4} + \dfrac{9}{16}$

$= 2 + \dfrac{9}{4} + \dfrac{9}{16}$

$= 2 + 2\dfrac{1}{4} + \dfrac{9}{16}$

$= 2 + 2\dfrac{4}{16} + \dfrac{9}{16}$

$= 4\dfrac{13}{16}$

Area $= 4\dfrac{13}{16}$ ft^2

3. Zikera is putting carpet in her house. She wants to carpet her living room, which measures 12 ft $\times 10\frac{1}{2}$ ft. She also wants to carpet her bedroom, which is 10 ft $\times 7\frac{1}{2}$ ft. How many square feet of carpet will she need to cover both rooms?

Area of the living room:

12 ft $\times 10\dfrac{1}{2}$ ft

$(12 \times 10) + \left(12 \times \dfrac{1}{2}\right)$

$= 120 + 6$

$= 126$

Area $= 126$ ft^2

> I find the area of the living room by multiplying the length and width. It is 126 square feet.

Area of the bedroom:

10 ft $\times 7\dfrac{1}{2}$ ft

$10 \times \dfrac{15}{2}$

$= \dfrac{150}{2}$

$= 75$

Area $= 75$ ft^2

> I find the area of the bedroom by multiplying the length and width. It is 75 square feet.

126 ft^2 + 75 ft^2 = 201 ft^2

She will need 201 square feet of carpet to cover both rooms.

> I combine both the area of both rooms to find the total area. The total is 201 square feet.

EUREKA
MATH™

G5-M5-Lesson 13

1. Find the area of the following rectangles. Draw an area model if it helps you.

   a. $\frac{35}{4}$ ft $\times 2\frac{3}{7}$ ft

   > I can use multiplication to find the area.

   $\frac{35}{4} \times \frac{17}{7}$

   > I can rename $2\frac{3}{7}$ as a fraction greater than one, $\frac{17}{7}$.

   $= \frac{{}^{5}35 \times 17}{4 \times 7^{1}}$

   > 35 and 7 have a common factor of 7. $35 \div 7 = 5$, and $7 \div 7 = 1$. The new numerator is 5×17, and the denominator is 4×1.

   $= \frac{5 \times 17}{4 \times 1}$

   $= \frac{85}{4}$

   > I can use division to convert from a fraction to a mixed number. 85 divided by 4 is equal to $21\frac{1}{4}$.

   $= 21\frac{1}{4}$

   $\text{Area} = 21\frac{1}{4}\,\text{ft}^2$

   b. $4\frac{2}{3}$ m $\times 2\frac{3}{5}$ m

   > I use the area model to solve this problem.

   > I can multiply to find all four partial products.
   > $2\,\text{m} \times 4\,\text{m} = 8\,\text{m}^2$
   > $2\,\text{m} \times \frac{2}{3}\,\text{m} = \frac{4}{3}\,\text{m}^2 = 1\frac{1}{3}\,\text{m}^2$
   > $\frac{3}{5}\,\text{m} \times 4\,\text{m} = \frac{12}{5}\,\text{m}^2 = 2\frac{2}{5}\,\text{m}^2$
   > $\frac{3}{5}\,\text{m} \times \frac{2}{3}\,\text{m} = \frac{6}{15}\,\text{m}^2$

   > I can add all four partial products to find the area.

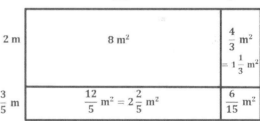

   $8\,\text{m}^2 + 1\frac{1}{3}\,\text{m}^2 + 2\frac{2}{5}\,\text{m}^2 + \frac{6}{15}\,\text{m}^2$

   $= 11\,\text{m}^2 + \frac{1}{3}\,\text{m}^2 + \frac{2}{5}\,\text{m}^2 + \frac{6}{15}\,\text{m}^2$

   $= 11\,\text{m}^2 + \frac{5}{15}\,\text{m}^2 + \frac{6}{15}\,\text{m}^2 + \frac{6}{15}\,\text{m}^2$

   $= 11\,\text{m}^2 + \frac{17}{15}\,\text{m}^2$

   $= 11\,\text{m}^2 + 1\frac{2}{15}\,\text{m}^2$

   $= 12\frac{2}{15}\,\text{m}^2$

   $\text{Area} = 12\frac{2}{15}\,\text{m}^2$

2. Meigan is cutting rectangles out of fabric to make a quilt. If the rectangles are $4\frac{3}{4}$ inches long and $2\frac{1}{2}$ inches wide, what is the area of five such rectangles?

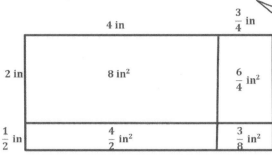

I can find the area of 1 rectangle, and then multiply by 5 to find the total area of 5 rectangles.

I draw an area model to help solve for the area of 1 rectangle.

I can add up the four partial products. The area of 1 rectangle is $11\frac{7}{8}$ square inches.

$$4\frac{3}{4} \times 2\frac{1}{2}$$

$$= (4 \times 2) + \left(4 \times \frac{1}{2}\right) + \left(\frac{3}{4} \times 2\right) + \left(\frac{3}{4} \times \frac{1}{2}\right)$$

$$= 8 + \frac{4}{2} + \frac{6}{4} + \frac{3}{8}$$

$$= 8 + 2 + 1\frac{2}{4} + \frac{3}{8}$$

$$= 11 + \frac{4}{8} + \frac{3}{8}$$

$$= 11\frac{7}{8}$$

$$1\ unit = 11\frac{7}{8}\ in^2$$

$$5\ units = 5 \times 11\frac{7}{8}\ in^2$$

The area of 1 rectangle or 1 unit is equal to $11\frac{7}{8}$ square inches. I can multiply by 5 to find the area of 5 rectangles or 5 units.

$$(5 \times 11) + \left(5 \times \frac{7}{8}\right)$$

$$= 55 + \frac{35}{8}$$

$$= 55 + 4\frac{3}{8}$$

$$= 59\frac{3}{8}$$

The area of five rectangles is $59\frac{3}{8}$ square inches.

EUREKA
MATH

©2015 Great Minds. eureka-math.org
G5-M1-HWH-1.3.0-07.2015

G5-M5-Lesson 14

1. Sam decided to paint a wall with two windows. The gray areas below show where the windows are. The windows will not be painted. Both windows are $2\frac{1}{2}$ ft by $4\frac{1}{2}$ ft rectangles. Find the area the paint needs to cover.

$13\frac{1}{2}$ ft

> I can subtract the area of the two windows from the area of the wall to find the area that the paint needs to cover.

9 ft

Area of 1 window:

$$2\frac{1}{2} \text{ ft} \times 4\frac{1}{2} \text{ ft}$$

$$\frac{5}{2} \times \frac{9}{2}$$

$$= \frac{45}{4}$$

$$= 11\frac{1}{4}$$

$$\text{Area} = 11\frac{1}{4} \text{ ft}^2$$

> The area of 1 window is $11\frac{1}{4}$ ft^2.

Area of 2 windows:

$$1 \text{ unit} = 11\frac{1}{4} \text{ ft}^2$$

$$2 \text{ units} = 2 \times 11\frac{1}{4} \text{ ft}^2$$

$$(2 \times 11) + \left(2 \times \frac{1}{4}\right)$$

$$= 22 + \frac{2}{4}$$

$$= 22\frac{1}{2}$$

$$\text{Area} = 22\frac{1}{2} \text{ ft}^2$$

> I can double the area of 1 window to find the area of 2 windows. The total area is $22\frac{1}{2}$ ft^2.

Area of the wall:

$$13\frac{1}{2} \text{ ft} \times 9 \text{ ft}$$

$$(13 \times 9) + \left(\frac{1}{2} \times 9\right)$$

$$= 117 + \frac{9}{2}$$

$$= 117 + 4\frac{1}{2}$$

$$= 121\frac{1}{2}$$

$$\text{Area} = 121\frac{1}{2} \text{ ft}^2$$

> I can subtract the area of the 2 windows from the area of the wall.

$$121\frac{1}{2} \text{ ft}^2 - 22\frac{1}{2} \text{ ft}^2 = 99 \text{ ft}^2$$

The paint needs to cover 99 square feet.

Lesson 14: Solve real world problems involving area of figures with fractional side lengths using visual models and/or equations.   27

©2015 Great Minds. eureka-math.org
G5-M1-HWH-1.3.0-07.2015

2. Mason uses square tiles, some of which he cuts in half, to make the figure below. If each square tile has a side length of $3\frac{1}{2}$ inches, what is the total area of the figure?

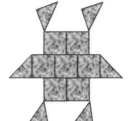

Total tiles:

7 whole tiles + *6 half tiles* = *10 tiles*

> I can count the tiles in the figure. There are a total of 10 tiles.

Area of 1 *tile:*

$3\frac{1}{2}$ in × $3\frac{1}{2}$ in

$\dfrac{7}{2} \times \dfrac{7}{2}$

$= \dfrac{49}{4}$

$= 12\dfrac{1}{4}$

> I can find the area of 1 square tile.
> $3\frac{1}{2}$ in × $3\frac{1}{2}$ in = $12\frac{1}{4}$ in².

Area = $12\dfrac{1}{4}$ in²

Area of 10 *tiles:*

> To find the area of 10 tiles, I can multiply the area of 1 tile by 10.

1 *unit* = $12\frac{1}{4}$ in²

10 *units* = $10 \times 12\frac{1}{4}$ in²

$(10 \times 12) + \left(10 \times \dfrac{1}{4}\right)$

$= 120 + \dfrac{10}{4}$

$= 120 + 2\dfrac{2}{4}$

$= 122\dfrac{1}{2}$

The total area of the figure is $122\frac{1}{2}$ *square inches.*

28   **Lesson 14:**   Solve real world problems involving area of figures with fractional side
                            lengths using visual models and/or equations.

EUREKA MATH™

©2015 Great Minds. eureka-math.org
G5-M1-HWH-1.3.0-07.2015

G5-M5-Lesson 15

1. The length of a flowerbed is 3 times as long as its width. If the width is $\frac{4}{5}$ meter, what is the area of the flowerbed?

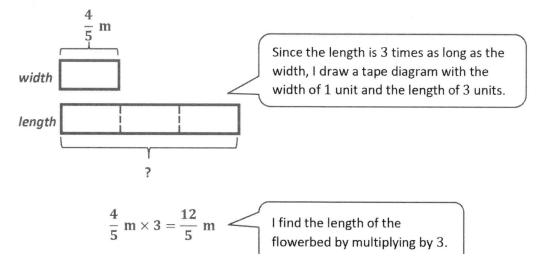

$$\frac{4}{5} \text{ m} \times 3 = \frac{12}{5} \text{ m}$$

I find the length of the flowerbed by multiplying by 3.

Area = length × width

$$= \frac{12}{5} \text{ m} \times \frac{4}{5} \text{ m}$$

I find the area of the flowerbed by multiplying the length times the width.

$$= \frac{48}{25} \text{ m}^2$$

$$= 1\frac{23}{25} \text{ m}^2$$

The flowerbed's area is $1\frac{23}{25}$ square meters.

EUREKA MATH Lesson 15: Solve real world problems involving area of figures with fractional side lengths using visual models and/or equations.   29

©2015 Great Minds. eureka-math.org
G5-M1-HWH-1.3.0-07.2015

2. Mrs. Tran grows herbs in square plots. Her rosemary plot measures $\frac{5}{6}$ yd on each side.

a. Find the total area of the rosemary plot.

$$\text{Area} = \text{length} \times \text{width}$$
$$= \frac{5}{6} \text{ yd} \times \frac{5}{6} \text{ yd}$$
$$= \frac{25}{36} \text{ yd}^2$$

> I multiply length times width to find the area of the rosemary plot.

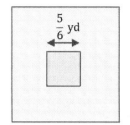

The total area of the rosemary plot is $\frac{25}{36}$ square yards.

b. Mrs. Tran puts a fence around the rosemary. If the fence is 2 ft from the edge of the garden on each side, what is the perimeter of the fence?

$$\frac{5}{6} \text{ yd} = \frac{5}{6} \times 1 \text{ yd}$$
$$= \frac{5}{6} \times 3 \text{ ft}$$
$$= \frac{15}{6} \text{ ft}$$
$$= 2\frac{3}{6} \text{ ft}$$
$$= 2\frac{1}{2} \text{ ft}$$

> I notice the unit here is feet, but the area I found from part (a) above was in yards.

> I convert the $\frac{5}{6}$ yard into feet. The length of the rosemary plot is $2\frac{1}{2}$ feet.

One side of the fence:

$$2\frac{1}{2} \text{ ft} + 4 \text{ ft} = 6\frac{1}{2} \text{ ft}$$

> I now find the length of one side of the fence. Since the fence is 2 feet from the edge of the garden on each side, I add 4 feet to the side of the rosemary plot, $2\frac{1}{2}$ feet. Each side of the fence is $6\frac{1}{2}$ feet long.

Perimeter of the fence:

$$6\frac{1}{2} \text{ ft} \times 4$$

> I multiply one side of the fence, $6\frac{1}{2}$ feet, by 4 to find the perimeter.

$$= (6 \text{ ft} \times 4) + \left(\frac{1}{2} \text{ ft} \times 4\right)$$
$$= 24 \text{ ft} + \frac{4}{2} \text{ ft}$$
$$= 24 \text{ ft} + 2 \text{ ft}$$
$$= 26 \text{ ft}$$

The perimeter of the fence is 26 feet.

Lesson 15: Solve real world problems involving area of figures with fractional side lengths using visual models and/or equations.   **EUREKA MATH**

G5-M5-Lesson 16

1. What are polygons with four sides called?

    Quadrilaterals

    > I know that the prefix "quad" means "four."

2. What are the attributes of trapezoids?

    - *They are quadrilaterals.*

    > I know that some trapezoids with more specific attributes are commonly known as parallelograms, rectangles, squares, rhombuses, and kites. But *ALL* trapezoids are quadrilaterals with at least one set of opposite sides parallel.

    - *They have at least one set of opposite sides parallel.*

    > I know that some trapezoids have only right angles (90°), some have two acute angles (less than 90°) and two obtuse angles (more than 90° but less than 180°), and some have a combination of right, acute, and obtuse angles.

3. Use a straightedge and the grid paper to draw

    a. A trapezoid with 2 sides of equal length.

    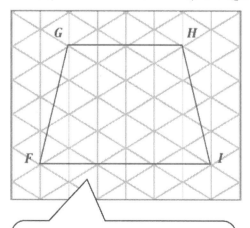

    > Since this trapezoid has 2 sides of equal length ($\overline{FG}$ and $\overline{HI}$), it is called an isosceles trapezoid.

    b. A trapezoid with no sides of equal length.

    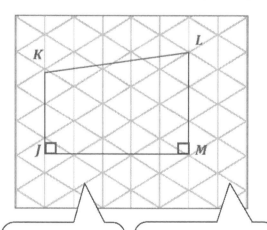

    > $\angle J$ and $\angle M$ are right angles and measure 90°.

    > In this trapezoid, none of the sides are equal in length.

G5-M5-Lesson 17

1. Circle all of the words that could be used to name the figure below.

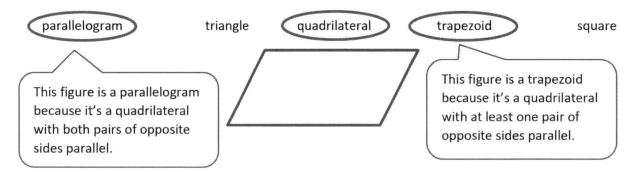

parallelogram   triangle   quadrilateral   trapezoid   square

This figure is a parallelogram because it's a quadrilateral with both pairs of opposite sides parallel.

This figure is a trapezoid because it's a quadrilateral with at least one pair of opposite sides parallel.

2. $HIJK$ is a parallelogram not drawn to scale.

   a. Using what you know about parallelograms, give the lengths of $\overline{KJ}$ and $\overline{HK}$.

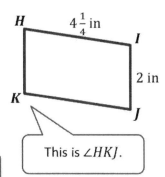

   $KJ = $ ___$4\frac{1}{4}$ in___ $HK = $ ___2 in___

   I know that opposite sides of a parallelogram are equal in length. $HI = KJ$.

   This is $\angle HKJ$.

   b. $\angle HKJ = 99°$. Use what you know about angles in a parallelogram to find the measure of the other angles.

   I know that opposite angles of a parallelograms are equal in measure.

   $\angle IHK = $ ___81___ ° $\angle JIH = $ ___99___ ° $\angle KJI = $ ___81___ °

   I know that angles that are next to one another, or adjacent, add up to 180°.
   $180° - 99° = 81°$

Lesson 17:   Draw parallelograms to clarify their attributes, and define parallelograms based on those attributes.   **EUREKA MATH**

©2015 Great Minds. eureka-math.org
G5-M1-HWH-1.3.0-07.2015

3. *PQRS* is a parallelogram not drawn to scale. $PR = 10$ mm and $MS =$ 4.5 mm. Give the lengths of the following segments:

$PM = \underline{\quad 5\ mm \quad}$ $QS = \underline{\quad 9\ mm \quad}$

> I know that the diagonals of a parallelogram bisect, or cut one another in two equal parts. So the length of $\overline{PM}$ is equal to half the length of $\overline{PR}$.

EUREKA MATH   Lesson 17:   Draw parallelograms to clarify their attributes, and define parallelograms based on those attributes.   33

©2015 Great Minds. eureka-math.org
G5-M1-HWH-1.3.0-07.2015

G5-M5-Lesson 18

1. What is the definition of a rhombus? Draw an example.

   A rhombus is a quadrilateral (a shape with 4 sides) with all sides equal in length.

   One example of a rhombus looks like this:

   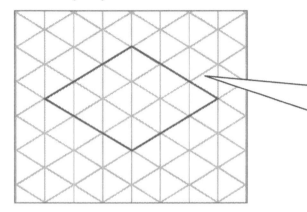

   My rhombus looks like a diamond, but I could have drawn it other ways, too. As long as it is a quadrilateral with 4 sides of equal length, it is a rhombus.

2. What is the definition of a rectangle? Draw an example.

   A rectangle is a quadrilateral with four right (90 degree) angles.

   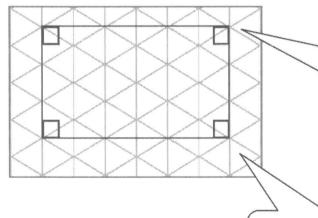

   My rectangle has 2 long sides and 2 short sides, but I could have drawn it other ways, too. As long as it is a quadrilateral with 4 right angles, it is a rectangle.

   The boxes in the corners of my rectangle show that all the angles are 90 degrees.

EUREKA MATH

G5-M5-Lesson 19

1. What are the attributes of a square? Draw an example.

    The attributes of a square are

    - *Four sides that are equal in length (same as a rhombus)*

    - *Four right angles (same as a rectangle)*

    - *A square is a type of rhombus and a type of rectangle!*

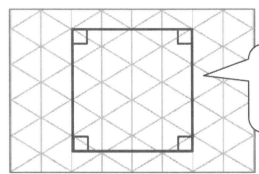

This is a square.

It is also a rhombus because it has 4 sides of equal length.

It is also a rectangle because it has 4 right angles.

2. What are the attributes of a kite? Draw an example.

    The attributes of a kite are

    - *A quadrilateral in which 2 consecutive (next to each other) sides are equal in length.*

    - *The other 2 side lengths are equal to one another as well.*

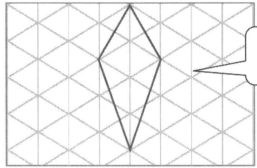

The 2 sides on "top" are equal in length, and the 2 sides on the "bottom" are equal in length.

EUREKA MATH   **Lesson 19:**   Draw kites and squares to clarify their attributes, and define kites and squares based on those attributes.   35

©2015 Great Minds. eureka-math.org
G5-M1-HWH-1.3.0-07.2015

3. Is the kite you drew in Problem 2, a parallelogram? Why or why not?

No, the kite I drew is not a parallelogram. A parallelogram must have both sets of opposite sides parallel. There are no parallel sides in my kite. The only time a kite is a parallelogram is when the kite is a square or a rhombus.

Lesson 19:   Draw kites and squares to clarify their attributes, and define kites and
                                    squares based on those attributes.

©2015 Great Minds. eureka-math.org
G5-M1-HWH-1.3.0-07.2015

EUREKA MATH™

G5-M5-Lesson 20

1. Fill in the table below.

Shape	Defining Attributes
Trapezoid	• Quadrilateral • Has at least one pair of parallel sides
Parallelogram	• *A quadrilateral in which both pairs of opposite sides are parallel*
Rectangle	• A quadrilateral with 4 right angles
Rhombus	• A quadrilateral with all sides of equal length
Square	• A rhombus with four 90° angles • A rectangle with 4 equal sides
Kite	• *Quadrilateral with 2 consecutive sides of equal length* • *Has 2 remaining sides of equal length*

2. $TUVW$ is a square with an area of 81 cm^2, and $UB = 6.36$ cm. Find the measurements using what you know about the properties of squares.

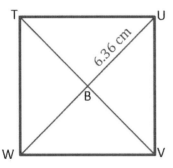

a. $UW = $ __12.72__ cm

> Diagonals of a square bisect each other, so $\overline{UB}$ and $\overline{BW}$ are equal in length. $6.36 + 6.36 = 12.72$

b. $TV = UW = 12.72$ cm

> I know that in a square the diagonals are equal in length.

c. Perimeter = __36__ cm

> I know that in a square every side length is equal, so I need to think about what times itself is equal to 81. I know that 9×9 is 81, so each side is 9 cm. Since there are 4 equal sides, I can multiply 9×4 to get the perimeter.

d. $m\angle TUV = $ __90__ °

> I know every angle in a square must be 90° because it is a defining attribute of a square.

G5-M5-Lesson 21

Finish each sentence below by writing "sometimes" or "always" in the first blank, and then state the reason why. Sketch an example of each statement in the space to the right.

a. A rectangle is *sometimes* a square because *a rectangle has 4 right angles, and a square is a special type of rectangle with 4 equal sides.*

> This is a rectangle. It is **not** a square because all 4 sides are not equal in length.

b. A square is *always* a rectangle because *a rectangle is a parallelogram with 4 right angles. A square is a rectangle with 4 equal sides.*

> This is a square and a rectangle because it has 4 right angles and 4 equal sides.

c. A rectangle is *sometimes* a kite because *a square fits the definition of a kite and rectangle. A kite has two pairs of sides that are equal, which is the same as a square.*

> This is a kite, a square, and a rectangle. It has 4 right angles and 2 sets of consecutive sides equal in length.

d. A rectangle is *always* a parallelogram because *it has two pairs of parallel sides*.

> All rectangles can also be called parallelograms.

e. A square is *always* a trapezoid because *it has at least one pair of parallel sides.*

> This square, and all squares, has 2 pairs of opposite sides that are parallel. All squares can also be called trapezoids.

f. A trapezoid is *sometimes* a parallelogram because *a trapezoid has to have at least one pair of parallel sides, but it could have two pairs, which fits the definition of a parallelogram.*

> This figure is a trapezoid but **not** a parallelogram. It only has 1 pair of opposite sides parallel. (The "top" and "bottom" sides are parallel.)

Lesson 21:   Draw and identify varied two-dimensional figures from given attributes.

Homework Helpers

Grade 5
Module 6

G5-M6-Lesson 1

1. Answer the following questions using number line P, below.

   > The origin is always zero.

   a. What is the coordinate, or the distance from the origin, of the ⬟ ?

      20

      > The coordinate tells the distance from the zero to the shape on the number line.

   b. What is the coordinate of ▲ ?

      25

   c. What is the coordinate at the midpoint between ❨ and ⬟ ?

      15

      > The distance from the moon to the pentagon is 10 units, so the midpoint will be 5 units from each shape.

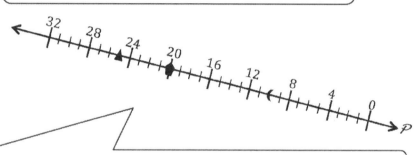

   > This number line increases from right to left. Number lines can go in any direction.

2. Use the number line to answer the questions.

   > The first tick mark is 0, and the second is 0.4. The distance between tick marks is 0.4, or $\frac{4}{10}$.

   a. Plot P so its distance is $\frac{2}{10}$ from the origin.

   b. Plot Q 12 tenths farther from the origin than point P.

      > 12 tenths more than 2 tenths is 14 tenths, or 1.4.

   c. Plot R so its distance is 1 closer to the origin than point Q.

   d. What is the distance from P to R?

      > I can think of 1 as 10 tenths.

      The distance from P to R is 0.2.

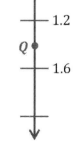

3. Number line L shows 18 units. Use number line L, below, to answer the questions.

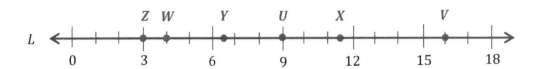

a. Plot a point at 3. Label it Z.

b. Label point Y at point $6\frac{1}{2}$.

> The units are one, and they are indicated by the tick marks on the number line.

> "Closer to the origin" means I have to move to the left along this number line.

c. Plot a point X that is 5 units farther from zero than point Y.

d. Plot W $\frac{5}{2}$ closer to the origin than point Y. What is the coordinate of point W?

The coordinate of point W is 4.

e. What is the coordinate of the point that is 4.5 units farther from the origin than point X? Label this point V.

The coordinate of point V is 16.

> $11\frac{1}{2} + 4\frac{1}{2} = 16$

f. Label point U midway between point Y and point X. What is the coordinate of this point?

The coordinate midway between points Y and X is 9.

4. A pirate buried stolen treasure in a vacant lot. He made a note that he buried the treasure 15 feet from the only tree on the lot. Later he could not find the treasure. What did he do wrong?

He did not indicate what direction from the tree he buried the treasure. If he just says fifteen feet from the tree, he'd have to dig a circle around the tree to find the treasure.

EUREKA MATH™

G5-M6-Lesson 2

1. Use a set square to draw a line perpendicular to the x-axis through point R. Label the new line as the y-axis.

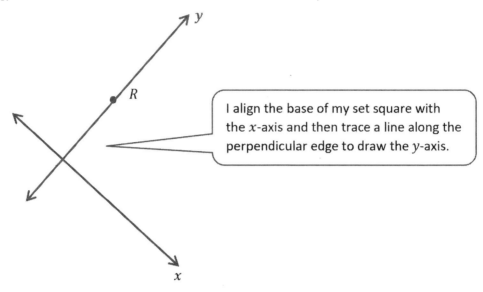

> I align the base of my set square with the x-axis and then trace a line along the perpendicular edge to draw the y-axis.

2. Use the perpendicular lines below to create a coordinate plane. Mark 6 units on each axis, and label them as fractions.

> I chose fractional units of $\frac{1}{2}$, but I could have chosen any fractional unit.

3. Use the coordinate plane to answer the following.

x-coordinate	y-coordinate	Shape
$1\frac{1}{2}$	0	circle
4.5	1.5	trapezoid
2	3	flag
3	4	square

$1\frac{1}{2}$ is not one of the numbers on the x-axis, but I know that $1\frac{1}{2}$ falls halfway between 1 and 2.

a. Name the shape at each location.

b. What shape is 3 units from the x-axis?

   The flag is 3 units from the x-axis.

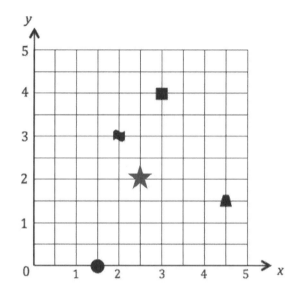

c. Which shape has a y-coordinate of 3?

   The flag has a y-coordinate of 3.

Problems 3(b) and 3(c) are asking the same question in different ways.

d. Draw a star at $\left(2\frac{1}{2}, 2\right)$.

The numbers in the parentheses are *coordinate pairs*. Coordinate pairs are written in parentheses with a comma separating the two coordinates. The *x-coordinate* is given first.

Lesson 2:   Construct a coordinate system on a plane.

EUREKA
MATH

G5-M6-Lesson 3

The y-axis is a vertical line. The x-axis is a horizontal line.

The origin, or $(0,0)$, is where the x- and y-axes meet.

1. Use the grid below to complete the following tasks.

    a. Construct a y-axis that passes through points A and B. Label this axis.

    b. Construct an x-axis that is perpendicular to the y-axis that passes through points A and M.

    c. Label the origin.

    d. The x-coordinate of point W is $2\frac{3}{4}$. Label the whole numbers along the x-axis.

    e. Label the whole numbers along the y-axis.

I find point W on the coordinate plane. I can trace down with my finger to locate this spot on the x-axis. I count back to 0 and see that each line on the grid is $\frac{1}{4}$ more than the previous line.

The y-axis must be labeled the same way as the x-axis. On the x-axis, the distance between grid lines is $\frac{1}{4}$. I can use the same units for the y-axis.

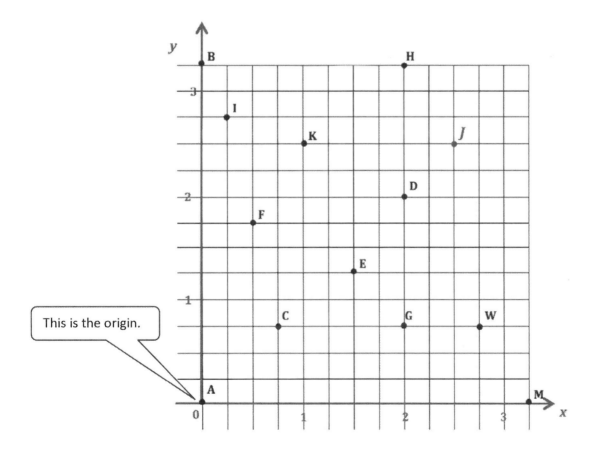

This is the origin.

EUREKA
MATH

Lesson 3:   Name points using coordinate pairs, and use the coordinate pairs to plot
points.

5

©2015 Great Minds. eureka-math.org
G5-M1-HWH-1.3.0-07.2015

2. For the following problems, consider all the points on the previous page.

   a. Identify all the points that have a y-coordinate of $\frac{3}{4}$.

      C, G, and W

      > I look for all of the points that are $\frac{3}{4}$ units from the x-axis.

   b. Identify all the points that have an x-coordinate of 2.

      G, D, and H

      > I look for points that are 2 units from the y-axis.

   c. Name the point, and write the coordinate pair that is $2\frac{1}{2}$ units above the x-axis and 1 unit to the right of the y-axis.

      $K\left(1, 2\frac{1}{2}\right)$

   d. Which point is located $1\frac{1}{4}$ units from the x-axis? Give its coordinates.

      $E\left(1\frac{1}{2}, 1\frac{1}{4}\right)$

   e. Which point is located $\frac{1}{4}$ units from the y-axis? Give its coordinates.

      $I\left(\frac{1}{4}, 2\frac{3}{4}\right)$

   f. Give the coordinates for point C.

      $\left(\frac{3}{4}, \frac{3}{4}\right)$

   g. Plot a point where both coordinates are the same. Label the point J, and give its coordinates.

      $\left(2\frac{1}{2}, 2\frac{1}{2}\right)$

      > There are infinite correct answers to this question. I could name coordinates that are not on the grid lines. For example, $(1.88, 1.88)$ would be correct.

   h. Name the point where the two axes intersect. Write the coordinates for this point.

      $A\,(0, 0)$

      > This point is also known as the origin. The axes meet at the origin.

Lesson 3:   Name points using coordinate pairs, and use the coordinate pairs to plot points.

EUREKA MATH

©2015 Great Minds. eureka-math.org
G5-M1-HWH-1.3.0-07.2015

i. What is the distance between points W and G, or WG?

$\frac{3}{4}$ *unit*

> I count the units between the points. The distance between each grid line is $\frac{1}{4}$.

j. Is the length of $\overline{HG}$ greater than, less than, or equal to $CG + KJ$?

$HG = 2\frac{1}{2}$ *units* $CG = 1\frac{1}{4}$ *units* $KJ = 1\frac{1}{2}$ *units* $CG + KJ = 2\frac{3}{4}$ *units* $HG < CG + KJ$

k. Janice described how to plot points on the coordinate plane. She said, "If you want to plot $(1, 3)$, go 1, and then go 3. Put a point where these lines intersect." Is Janice correct?

Janice is not correct. She should give a starting point and a direction. She should say, "Start at the origin. Along the x-axis, go 1 unit to the right, and then go up 3 units parallel to the y-axis."

G5-M6-Lesson 4

Lesson Notes

The rules for playing *Battleship*, a popular game, are at the end of this Homework Helper.

1. While playing *Battleship*, your friend says, "Hit!" when you guess point $(3,2)$. How do you decide which points to guess next?

   If I get a hit at point $(3,2)$, then I know I should try to guess one of the four points around $(3,2)$ because the ship has to lie either vertically or horizontally according to the rules. I would guess one of these points: $(2,2)$, $(3,1)$, $(4,2)$, or $(3,3)$.

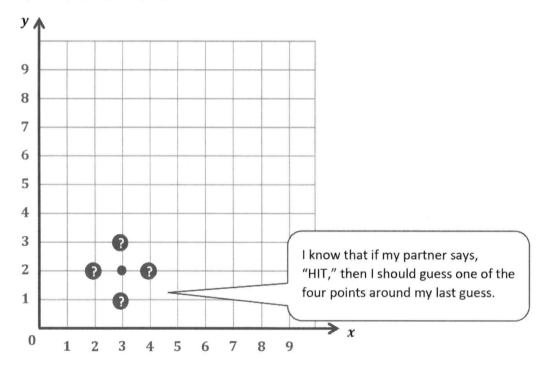

   I know that if my partner says, "HIT," then I should guess one of the four points around my last guess.

2. What changes to the game could make it more challenging?

   The game is easiest when I count by ones on the coordinate grid's axes. If I changed the axes to count by another number like 7's or 9's on each grid line, the game would be more challenging. It would also be more challenging if I skip-count on the axes by fractions such as $\frac{1}{2}$ or $2\frac{1}{2}$.

©2015 Great Minds. eureka-math.org
G5-M1-HWH-1.3.0-07.2015

Battleship Rules

Goal: To sink all of your opponent's ships by correctly guessing their coordinates.

Materials
- 1 My Ships grid sheet (per person/per game)
- 1 Enemy Ships grid sheet (per person/per game)
- Red crayon/marker for hits
- Black crayon/marker for misses
- Folder to place between players

Ships
- Each player must mark 5 ships on the grid.
    - Aircraft Carrier—Plot 5 points
    - Battleship—Plot 4 points
    - Cruiser—Plot 3 points
    - Submarine—Plot 3 points
    - Patrol Boat—Plot 2 points

Setup
- With your opponent, choose a unit length and fractional unit for the coordinate plane.
- Label chosen units on both grid sheets.
- Secretly select locations for each of the 5 ships on your My Ships grid.
    - All ships must be placed horizontally or vertically on the coordinate plane.
    - Ships can touch each other, but they may not occupy the same coordinate.

Play
- Players take turns firing one shot to attack enemy ships.
- On your turn, call out the coordinates of your attacking shot. Record the coordinates of each attack shot.
- Your opponent checks his My Ships grid. If that coordinate is unoccupied, your opponent says, "Miss." If you named a coordinate occupied by a ship, your opponent says, "Hit."
- Mark each attempted shot on your Enemy Ships grid. Mark a black ✖ on the coordinate if your opponent says, "Miss." Mark a red ✓ on the coordinate if your opponent says, "Hit."
- On your opponent's turn, if he hits one of your ships, mark a red ✓on that coordinate of your My Ships grid. When one of your ships has every coordinate marked with a ✓, say, "You've sunk my [name of ship]."

Victory
- The first player to sink all (or the most) opposing ships wins.

G5-M6-Lesson 5

1. Use the coordinate plane to answer the questions.

    a. Use a straight edge to construct a line that goes through points Z and Y. Label this line j.

    b. Line j is perpendicular to the __x__-axis, and is parallel to the __y__-axis.

    > Parallel lines will never cross.

    > Perpendicular lines form 90° angles.

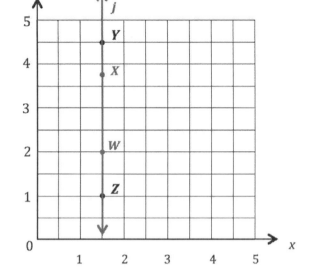

    c. Draw two more points on line j. Name these points X and W.

    d. Give the coordinates of each point below.

2.

    a. W: $\left(1\frac{1}{2}, 2\right)$ X: $\left(1\frac{1}{2}, 3\frac{3}{4}\right)$ Y: $\left(1\frac{1}{2}, 4\frac{1}{2}\right)$ Z: $\left(1\frac{1}{2}, 1\right)$

    b. What do all these points on line j have in common?

    The x-coordinate is always $1\frac{1}{2}$.

    > This line is perpendicular to the x-axis and parallel to the y-axis because the x-coordinate is the same in every coordinate pair.

    c. Give the coordinate pair of another point that falls on line j with a y-coordinate greater than 10.

    $\left(1\frac{1}{2}, 12\right)$

    > As long as the x-coordinate is $1\frac{1}{2}$, the point will fall on line j.

EUREKA
MATH™

©2015 Great Minds. eureka-math.org
G5-M1-HWH-1.3.0-07.2015

3. For each pair of points below, think about the line that joins them. Will the line be parallel to the x-axis or y-axis? Without plotting them, explain how you know.

   a. $(1.45, 2)$ and $(66, 2)$

   Since these coordinate pairs have the same y-coordinate, the line that joins them will be a horizontal line and parallel to the x-axis.

   b. $\left(\frac{1}{2}, 19\right)$ and $\left(\frac{1}{2}, 82\right)$

   Since these coordinate pairs have the same x-coordinate, the line that joins them will be a vertical line and parallel to the y-axis.

4. Write the coordinate pairs of 3 points that can be connected to construct a line that is $3\frac{1}{8}$ units above and parallel to the x-axis.

   $\left(7, 3\frac{1}{8}\right)$ $\left(6\frac{1}{8}, 3\frac{1}{8}\right)$ $\left(79, 3\frac{1}{8}\right)$

   In order for the line to be $3\frac{1}{8}$ units above the x-axis, the coordinate pairs must have a y-coordinate of $3\frac{1}{8}$. I can use any x-coordinate.

5. Write the coordinate pairs of 3 points that lie on the x-axis.

   $(7, 0)$ $(11.1, 0)$ $(100, 0)$

EUREKA
MATH™

Lesson 5:   Investigate patterns in vertical and horizontal lines, and interpret points   11
            on the plane as distances from the axes.

©2015 Great Minds. eureka-math.org
G5-M1-HWH-1.3.0-07.2015

G5-M6-Lesson 6

1. Plot and label the following points on the coordinate plane.

$K\ (0.7, 0.6)$ $P\ (0.7, 1.1)$ $M\ (0.2, 0.3)$ $H\ (0.9, 0.3)$

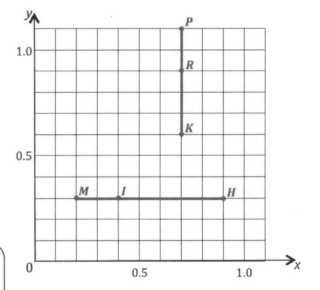

    a.   Use a straightedge to construct line segments KP and MH.

    b.   Name the line segment that is perpendicular to the x-axis and parallel to the y-axis.

        $\overline{KP}$

           Because the x-coordinates of K and P are the same, segment KP is parallel to the y-axis.

    c.   Name the line segment that is parallel to the x-axis and perpendicular to the y-axis.

        $\overline{MH}$

           Because the y-coordinates of M and H are the same, segment MH is perpendicular to the y-axis.

    d.   Plot a point on $\overline{KP}$, and name it R.

    e.   Plot a point on $\overline{MH}$, and name it I.

    f.   Write the coordinates for points R and I.

        $R\ (0.7, 0.9)$ $I\ (0.4, 0.3)$

Lesson 6:   Investigate patterns in vertical and horizontal lines, and interpret points on the plane as distances from the axes.

©2015 Great Minds. eureka-math.org
G5-M1-HWH-1.3.0-07.2015

EUREKA
MATH™

2. Construct line j such that the y-coordinate of every point is $2\frac{1}{4}$, and construct line k such that the x-coordinate of every point is $1\frac{3}{4}$.

> Since all the y-coordinates are the same, line j will be a horizontal line.
> Since all the x-coordinates are the same, line k will be a vertical line.

a. Line j is _____$2\frac{1}{4}$_____ units from the x-axis.

b. Give the coordinates of the point on line j that is 1 unit from the y-axis.

$\left(1, 2\frac{1}{4}\right)$

> "1 unit from the y-axis" gives the value of the x-coordinate.

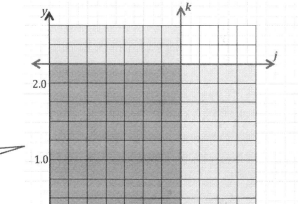

c. With a colored pencil, shade the portion of the grid that is less than $2\frac{1}{4}$ units from the x-axis.

> I use blue to shade the grid below line j.

d. Line k is _____$1\frac{3}{4}$_____ units from the y-axis.

e. Give the coordinates of the point on line k that is $1\frac{1}{2}$ units from the x-axis.

$\left(1\frac{3}{4}, 1\frac{1}{2}\right)$

> "$1\frac{1}{2}$ units from the x-axis" gives the value of the y-coordinate.

f. With another colored pencil, shade the portion of the grid that is less than $1\frac{3}{4}$ units from the y-axis.

> I use pink to shade the grid to the left of line k. The area of the grid that is below line j and to the left of line k now looks purple.

EUREKA MATH™   Lesson 6:   Investigate patterns in vertical and horizontal lines, and interpret points   **13**
on the plane as distances from the axes.

©2015 Great Minds. eureka-math.org
G5-M1-HWH-1.3.0-07.2015

G5-M6-Lesson 7

1. Complete the chart. Then, plot the points on the coordinate plane.

x	y	(x, y)
3	$1\frac{1}{2}$	$\left(3, 1\frac{1}{2}\right)$
$1\frac{1}{2}$	0	$\left(1\frac{1}{2}, 0\right)$
2	$\frac{1}{2}$	$\left(2, \frac{1}{2}\right)$
$4\frac{1}{2}$	3	$\left(4\frac{1}{2}, 3\right)$

a. Use a straightedge to draw a line connecting these points.

I could have also said that the y-coordinates are $1\frac{1}{2}$ less than the corresponding x-coordinates.

b. Write a rule showing the relationship between the x-coordinates and y-coordinates of points on this line.

Each x-coordinate is $1\frac{1}{2}$ more than its corresponding y-coordinate.

c. Name the coordinates of two other points that are also on this line.

$\left(2\frac{1}{2}, 1\right)$ *and* $\left(5, 3\frac{1}{2}\right)$

As long as the x-coordinate is $1\frac{1}{2}$ more than the y-coordinate, the point will fall on this line.

Lesson 7: Plot points, use them to draw lines in the plane, and describe patterns within the coordinate pairs.

EUREKA MATH

2. Complete the chart. Then, plot the points on the coordinate plane.

x	y	(x, y)
$\frac{3}{4}$	3	$\left(\frac{3}{4}, 3\right)$
1	4	$(1, 4)$
$\frac{1}{2}$	2	$\left(\frac{1}{2}, 2\right)$
0	0	$(0, 0)$

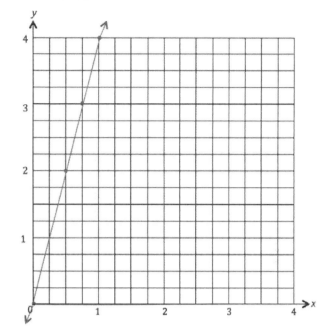

a. Use a straightedge to draw a line connecting these points.

b. Write a rule showing the relationship between the x-coordinates and y-coordinates for points on the line.

   Each y-coordinate is four times as much as its corresponding x-coordinate.

c. Name two other points that are also on this line.

   $(2, 8)$ *and* $\left(\frac{5}{8}, 2\frac{1}{2}\right)$

   > This rule is also correct: Each x-coordinate is 1 fourth as much as its corresponding y-coordinate.

EUREKA MATH   Lesson 7:   Plot points, use them to draw lines in the plane, and describe patterns within the coordinate pairs.   15

©2015 Great Minds. eureka-math.org
G5-M1-HWH-1.3.0-07.2015

3. Use the coordinate plane to answer the following questions.

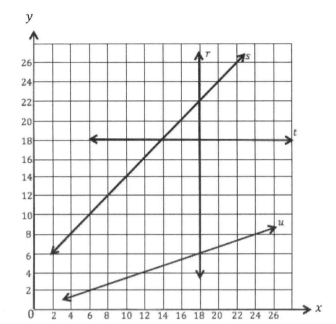

a. For any point on line r, the x-coordinate is __18__.

> The x-coordinate tells the distance from the y-axis.

b. Give the coordinates for 3 points that are on line s.

$(4, 8)$ $(10, 14)$ $(20, 24)$

c. Write a rule that describes the relationship between the x-coordinates and y-coordinates on line s.

Each y-coordinate is 4 more than its corresponding x-coordinate.

> I could also say, "Each x-coordinate is 4 less than the y-coordinate."

d. Give the coordinates for 3 points that are on line u.

$(6, 2)$ $(12, 4)$ $(24, 8)$

e. Write a rule that describes the relationship between the x-coordinates and y-coordinates on line u.

Each x-coordinate is 3 times as much as the y-coordinate.

> I could also say, "Each y-coordinate is $\frac{1}{3}$ the value of the x-coordinate."

f. Each of these points lies on at least 1 of the lines shown in the plane above. Identify a line that contains the following points.

$(18, 16.3)$ ___r___ $(9.5, 13.5)$ ___s___ $\left(16, 5\frac{1}{3}\right)$ ___u___ $(22.3, 18)$ ___t___

> All of the points on line r have an x-coordinate of 18.

> All of the points on line t have a y-coordinate of 18.

16   Lesson 7:   Plot points, use them to draw lines in the plane, and describe patterns
                           within the coordinate pairs.

                           EUREKA
                           MATH

©2015 Great Minds. eureka-math.org
G5-M1-HWH-1.3.0-07.2015

G5-M6-Lesson 8

Complete this table such that each y-coordinate is 5 more than the corresponding x-coordinate.

x	y	(x, y)
2	7	$(2, 7)$
4	9	$(4, 9)$
6	11	$(6, 11)$

I choose coordinate pairs that satisfy the rule and will fit on the coordinate plane.

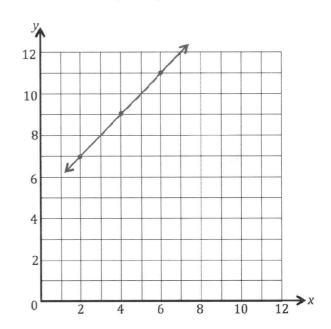

a. Plot each point on the coordinate plane.

b. Use a straightedge to construct a line connecting these points.

c. Give the coordinate of 3 other points that fall on this line with x-coordinates greater than 15.

$(17, 22)$ $\left(20\frac{1}{2}, 25\frac{1}{2}\right)$ $(100, 105)$

Although I can't see these points on the plane, I know they will fall on the line because each y-coordinate is 5 more than the x-coordinate.

G5-M6-Lesson 9

In order to find the y-coordinates, I just follow the rule, "y is 2 less than x."

So when x is 5, I find the number that is 2 less than 5. $5 - 2 = 3$.

So when x is 5, y is 3.

1. Complete the table with the given rules.

Line a

Rule: y is 2 less than x.

x	y	(x, y)
2	0	$(2, 0)$
5	3	$(5, 3)$
10	8	$(10, 8)$
17	15	$(17, 15)$

Line b

Rule: y is 4 less than x.

x	y	(x, y)
5	1	$(5, 1)$
8	4	$(8, 4)$
14	10	$(14, 10)$
20	16	$(20, 16)$

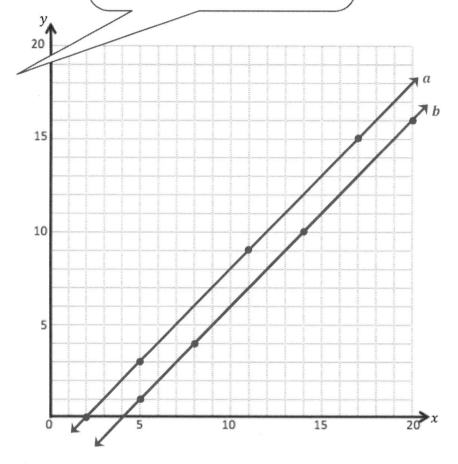

a. Construct each line on the coordinate plane.

b. Compare and contrast these lines.

   The lines are parallel. Neither line passes through the origin. Line b looks like it is closer to the x-axis or farther down and to the right. Line a is closer to the y-axis and farther up and to the left.

c. Based on the patterns you see, predict what line c, whose rule is y is 6 less than x, would look like.

   Since the rule for line c is also a subtraction rule, I think it will also be parallel to lines a and b. But, since the rule is "y is 6 less than x," I think it will be even farther to the right than line b.

©2015 Great Minds. eureka-math.org
G5-M1-HWH-1.3.0-07.2015

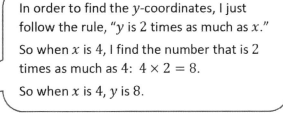

In order to find the y-coordinates, I just follow the rule, "y is 2 times as much as x." So when x is 4, I find the number that is 2 times as much as 4: $4 \times 2 = 8$. So when x is 4, y is 8.

2. Complete the table for the given rules.

Line e

Rule: y is 2 times as much as x.

x	y	(x, y)
0	0	$(0, 0)$
1	2	$(1, 2)$
4	8	$(4, 8)$
9	18	$(9, 18)$

Line f

Rule: y is half as much as x.

x	y	(x, y)
0	0	$(0, 0)$
6	3	$(6, 3)$
12	6	$(12, 6)$
18	9	$(18, 9)$

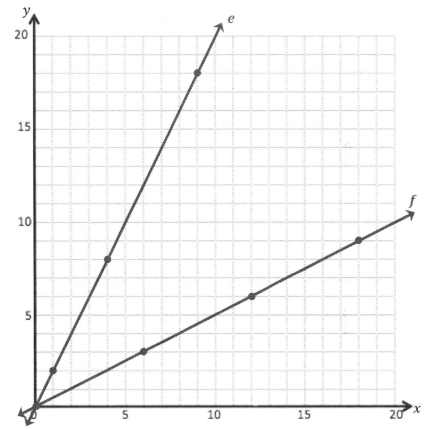

a.   Construct each line on the coordinate plane.

b.   Compare and contrast these lines.

Both lines go through the origin, and they are not parallel. Line e is steeper than line f.

c.   Based on the patterns you see, predict what line g, whose rule is y *is 3 times as much as x*, and line h, whose rule is y *is a third as much as x*, would look like.

Since the rule for line g is also a multiplication rule, I think it will also pass through the origin. But, since the rule is "y is 3 times as much as x," I think it will be even steeper than lines e and f.

Lesson 9: Generate two number patterns from given rules, plot the points, and analyze the patterns.

©2015 Great Minds. eureka-math.org
G5-M1-HWH-1.3.0-07.2015

19

G5-M6-Lesson 10

1. Use the coordinate plane to complete the following tasks.

a. The rule for line b is "x and y are equal."
Construct line b.

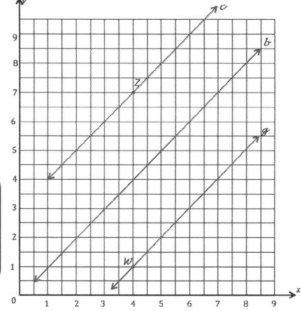

> Some coordinate pairs that follow this rule are
> $(1, 1)$ $(3, 3)$ $(6.5, 6.5)$

b. Construct a line, c, that is parallel to line b and contains point Z.

> Since line c needs to be parallel to line b, the rule for line c must be an addition or subtraction rule. The coordinate pair for Z is $(4, 7)$, so I can draw line c along other coordinate pairs that have a y-coordinate that is 3 *more* than the x-coordinate.

c. Name 3 coordinate pairs on line c.

$(2, 5)$ $(3, 6)$ $(6, 9)$

d. Identify a rule to describe line c.

> Another way to describe this rule is: y is 3 more than x.

x is 3 less than y.

e. Construct a line, g, that is parallel to line b and contains point W.

f. Name 3 points on line g.

$(3.5, 0.5)$ $(6, 3)$ $(7, 4)$

> Again, since line g needs to be parallel to line b, the rule for line g must be an addition or subtraction rule. The coordinate pair for W is $(4, 1)$, so I can draw line g along other coordinate pairs that have a y-coordinate that is 3 *less* than the x-coordinate.

g. Identify a rule to describe line g.

x is 3 more than y.

EUREKA
MATH™

©2015 Great Minds. eureka-math.org
G5-M1-HWH-1.3.0-07.2015

h.   Compare and contrast lines c and g in terms of their relationship to line b.

Lines c and g are both parallel to line b.
Line c is above line b because the points on line c have y-coordinates greater than the x-coordinates.
Line g is below line b because the points on line g have y-coordinates less than the x-coordinates.

2.   Write a rule for a fourth line that would be parallel to those in Problem 1 and that would contain the point $(5, 6)$.

y is 1 more than x.

> Because this line is parallel to the others, I know it has to be an addition rule. In the given coordinate pair, the y-coordinate is 1 more than the x-coordinate.

3.   Use the coordinate plane below to complete the following tasks.

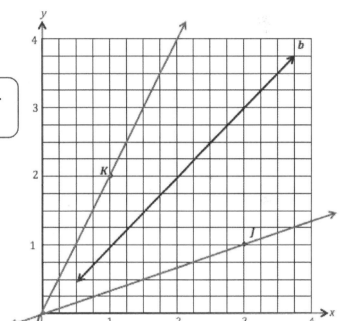

a.   Line b represents the rule "x and y are equal."

> I can also think of this as a multiplication rule. "x times 1 is equal to y."

b.   Construct a line, j, that contains the origin and point J.

c.   Name 3 points on line j.

$(3, 1)$ $\left(1\frac{1}{2}, \frac{1}{2}\right)$ $\left(\frac{3}{4}, \frac{1}{4}\right)$

d.   Identify a rule to describe line j.

x is 3 times as much as y.

> As I analyze the relationship between the x- and y-coordinates on line j, I can see that each y-coordinate is $\frac{1}{3}$ the value of its corresponding x-coordinate.

e. Construct a line, k, that contains the origin and point K.

f. Name 3 points on line k.

$\left(\frac{1}{2}, 1\right)$ $\left(1\frac{1}{2}, 3\right)$ $(2, 4)$

g. Identify a rule to describe line k.

x is half of y.

As I analyze the relationship between the x-coordinates and y-coordinates on line k, I can see that each y-coordinate is twice the value of its corresponding x-coordinate.

Lesson 10: Compare the lines and patterns generated by addition rules and multiplication rules.

G5-M6-Lesson 11

1. Complete the tables for the given rules.

Line p

Rule: *Halve x.*

x	y	(x, y)
2	1	$(2, 1)$
4	2	$(4, 2)$
6	3	$(6, 3)$

Line q

Rule: *Halve x, and then add 1.*

x	y	(x, y)
2	2	$(2, 2)$
4	3	$(4, 3)$
6	4	$(6, 4)$

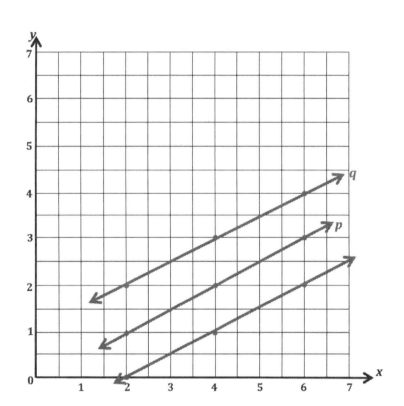

a. Draw each line on the coordinate plane above.

b. Compare and contrast these lines.

> Line q is *above* line p because the rule says, "*then add* 1."

They are parallel lines. Line q is above line p. The distance between the two lines is 1 unit.

c. Based on the patterns you see, predict what the line for the rule "halve x, and then subtract 1" would look like. Draw your prediction on the plane above.

I predict the line will be parallel to lines p and q.

It will be 1 unit below line p because the rule says, "then subtract 1."

©2015 Great Minds. eureka-math.org
G5-M1-HWH-1.3.0-07.2015

I need to look for coordinate pairs that follow the rule, "*double x, and then add $\frac{1}{2}$.*"

2. Circle the point(s) that the line for the rule "*double x, and then add $\frac{1}{2}$*" would contain.

$(0, 1)$ $\left(3, 6\frac{1}{2}\right)$ $\left(2, \frac{1}{2}\right)$ $\left(\frac{3}{4}, 2\right)$ $\left(0, \frac{1}{2}\right)$ $\left(2, 4\frac{1}{4}\right)$

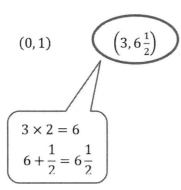

$3 \times 2 = 6$

$6 + \frac{1}{2} = 6\frac{1}{2}$

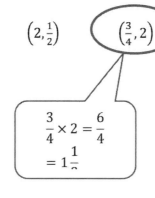

$\frac{3}{4} \times 2 = \frac{6}{4}$

$= 1\frac{1}{2}$

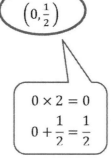

$0 \times 2 = 0$

$0 + \frac{1}{2} = \frac{1}{2}$

3. Give two other points that fall on this line.

$\left(\frac{1}{2}, 1\frac{1}{2}\right)$ $\left(1, 2\frac{1}{2}\right)$

I choose values for the x-coordinates. Then I doubled them and added $\frac{1}{2}$ to get the y-coordinates.

EUREKA
MATH

G5-M6-Lesson 12

1. Write a rule for the line that contains the points $(0.3, 0.5)$ and $(1.0, 1.2)$.

    y is 0.2 more than x.

    a. Identify 2 more points on this line. Then draw it on the grid below.

Point	x	y	(x, y)
E	0.7	0.9	$(0.7, 0.9)$
F	1.5	1.7	$(1.5, 1.7)$

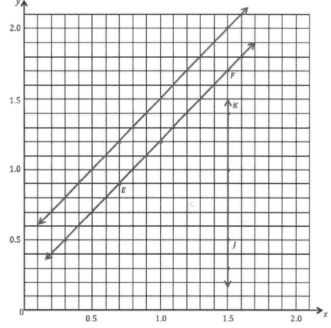

    b. Write a rule for a line that is parallel to $\overleftrightarrow{EF}$ and goes through point $(0.7, 1.2)$. Then draw the line on the grid.

    y is 0.5 more than x.

    > Since this line needs to be parallel to $\overleftrightarrow{EF}$, it must be an addition rule. In the coordinate pair $(0.7, 1.2)$, I can see that the y-coordinate is 0.5 more than the x-coordinate.

2. Give the rule for the line that contains the points $(1.5, 0.3)$ and $(1.5, 1.0)$.

    x is always 1.5.

    a. Identify 2 more points on this line. Draw the line on the grid above.

Point	x	y	(x, y)
J	1.5	0.5	$(1.5, 0.5)$
K	1.5	1.4	$(1.5, 1.4)$

    b. Write a rule for a line that is parallel to $\overleftrightarrow{JK}$.

    x is always 1.8.

    > Since this line must be parallel to $\overleftrightarrow{JK}$, it must be another vertical line where the x-coordinate is always the same.

©2015 Great Minds. eureka-math.org
G5-M1-HWH-1.3.0-07.2015

3. Give the rule for a line that contains the point $(0.3, 0.9)$ using the operation or description below. Then, name 2 other points that would fall on each line.

a. Addition: *y is 0.6 more than x.*

Point	x	y	(x, y)
T	0.4	1	$(0.4, 1)$
U	1	1.6	$(1, 1.6)$

b. A line parallel to the x-axis: *y is always 0.9.*

Point	x	y	(x, y)
G	0.4	0.9	$(0.4, 0.9)$
H	1	0.9	$(1, 0.9)$

> A line parallel to the x-axis is a horizontal line.
> Horizontal lines have y-coordinates that do not change.

c. Multiplication: *y is x tripled.*

Point	x	y	(x, y)
A	0.2	0.6	$(0.2, 0.6)$
B	0.5	1.5	$(0.5, 1.5)$

d. A line parallel to the y-axis: *x is always 0.3.*

Point	x	y	(x, y)
V	0.3	1.3	$(0.3, 1.3)$
W	0.3	2	$(0.3, 2)$

> A line parallel to the y-axis is a vertical line. Vertical lines have x-coordinates that do not change.

e. Multiplication with addition: *Double x, and then add 0.3.*

Point	x	y	(x, y)
R	0.4	1.1	$(0.4, 1.1)$
S	0.5	1.3	$(0.5, 1.3)$

> I can use the original coordinate pair, $(0.3, 0.9)$, to help me generate a multiplication with addition rule.
>
> $0.3 \times 2 = 0.6$ (This is the "*Double x*" part of the rule.)
>
> $0.6 + 0.3 = 0.9$ (This is the "*then add 0.3*" part of the rule.)

Lesson 12:   Create a rule to generate a number pattern, and plot the points.   EUREKA MATH™

©2015 Great Minds. eureka-math.org
G5-M1-HWH-1.3.0-07.2015

G5-M6-Lesson 13

1. Maya and Ruvio used their right angle templates and straightedges to draw sets of parallel lines. Who drew a correct set of parallel lines and why?

    Maya: **Ruvio:**

   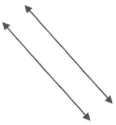   

   Maya drew a correct set of parallel lines because if you extend her lines, they will never intersect (cross). If you extend Ruvio's lines, they will intersect.

2. On the grid below, Maya circled all the sets of segments that she thought were parallel. Is she correct? Why or why not?

   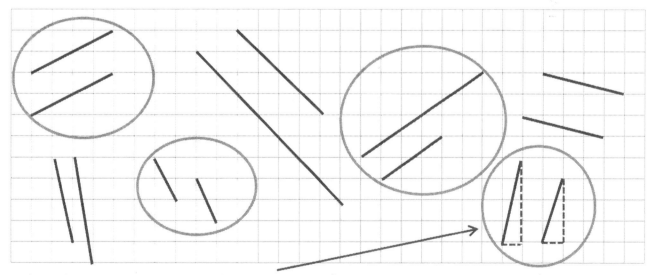

   Maya is not completely correct. This set is not parallel. I drew a horizontal and vertical dotted line near each segment to complete a triangle. Even though both triangles have a base of 1, the left triangle is taller. I can see that if I were to extend these segments, they would eventually intersect. These segments are not parallel. Also, Maya did not circle all of the parallel sets of segments.

3. Use your straightedge to draw a segment parallel to each segment through the given point.

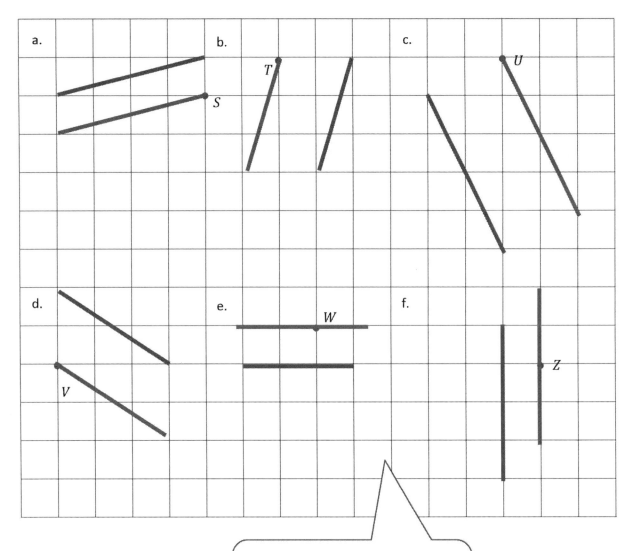

I know that the lines do not have to be exactly the same length as long as they are always the same distance apart at every point.

Lesson 13:   Construct parallel line segments on a rectangular grid.

©2015 Great Minds. eureka-math.org
G5-M1-HWH-1.3.0-07.2015

G5-M6-Lesson 14

1. Use the coordinate plane below to complete the following tasks.

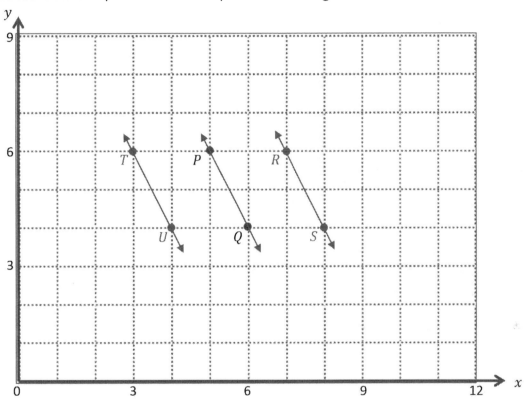

a. Identify the locations of P and Q. P (__5__ , __6__) Q (__6__ , __4__)

b. Draw $\overleftrightarrow{PQ}$.

> The symbol ⊥ means perpendicular.
> The symbol ∥ means parallel.

c. Plot the following coordinate pairs on the plane: R $(7,6)$ S $(8,4)$

d. Draw $\overleftrightarrow{RS}$.

e. Circle the relationship between $\overleftrightarrow{PQ}$ and $\overleftrightarrow{RS}$. $\overleftrightarrow{PQ} \perp \overleftrightarrow{RS}$

Lesson 14:   Construct parallel line segments, and analyze relationships of the   **29**
coordinate pairs.

©2015 Great Minds. eureka-math.org
G5-M1-HWH-1.3.0-07.2015

f. Give the coordinates of a pair of points, T and U, such that $\overleftrightarrow{TU} \parallel \overleftrightarrow{PQ}$.

   T (_3_ , _6_) U (_4_ , _4_)

   There are many possible sets of coordinates that would make $\overleftrightarrow{TU}$ parallel to $\overleftrightarrow{PQ}$. I can keep the y-coordinates the same and move the x-coordinates 2 units to the left.

g. Draw $\overleftrightarrow{TU}$.

2. Use the coordinate plane below to complete the following tasks.

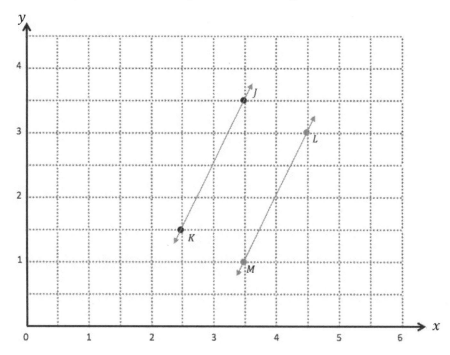

a. Identify the locations of J and K. $J \left(3\frac{1}{2}, 3\frac{1}{2}\right)$ $K \left(2\frac{1}{2}, 1\frac{1}{2}\right)$

b. Draw $\overleftrightarrow{JK}$.

c. Generate coordinate pairs for L and M such that $\overleftrightarrow{JK} \parallel \overleftrightarrow{LM}$. $L \left(4\frac{1}{2}, 3\right)$ $M \left(3\frac{1}{2}, 1\right)$

d. Draw $\overleftrightarrow{LM}$.

e. Explain the pattern you used when generating coordinate pairs for L and M.

   I visualized shifting points J and K one unit to the <u>right</u>, which is two grid lines. As a result, the x-coordinates of L and M are 1 greater than those of J and K.

   Then I visualized shifting both points <u>down</u> one-half unit, which is one grid line. As a result, the y-coordinates of L and M are $\frac{1}{2}$ less than those of J and K.

Lesson 14:   Construct parallel line segments, and analyze relationships of the coordinate pairs.   **EUREKA MATH**

©2015 Great Minds. eureka-math.org
G5-M1-HWH-1.3.0-07.2015

G5-M6-Lesson 15

Perpendicular segments intersect and form 90°, or right, angles.

1. Circle the pairs of segments that are perpendicular.

The angle formed by these segments is greater than 90°. These segments are *not* perpendicular.

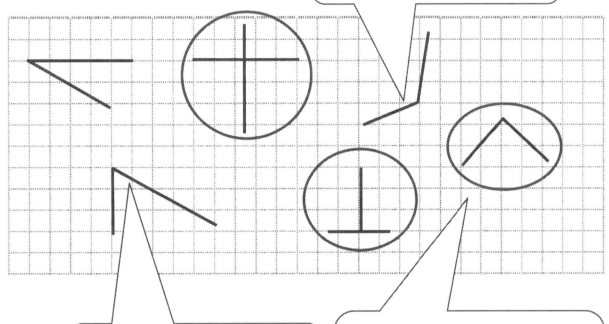

The angle formed by these segments is less than 90°. These segments are *not* perpendicular.

I can use anything that is a right angle, such as the corner of a paper, to see if it fits in the angle where the lines intersect. If it fits perfectly, then I know that the lines are perpendicular.

2. Draw a segment perpendicular to each given segment. Show your thinking by sketching triangles as needed.

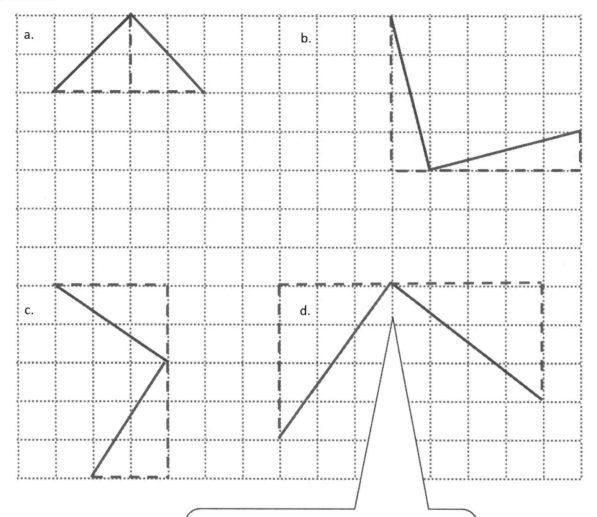

I can sketch 2 missing sides to create a triangle. Then if I visualize rotating it and sliding it, I can draw a perpendicular segment by sketching the longest side of the triangle.

G5-M6-Lesson 16

1. In the right triangle below, the measure of angle L is 50°. What is the measure of angle K?

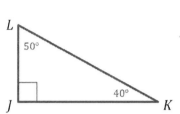

$\angle K = 40°$

The sum of the interior angles of *all* triangles is 180°. Triangle JKL is a right triangle. Since $\angle J$ is 90°, and $\angle L$ is 50°, $\angle K$ must be 40°.

$$180° - 90° - 50° = 40°$$

After I sketch the right triangle, I can visualize it sliding and rotating. These triangles are the same.

2. Use the coordinate plane below to complete the following tasks.

   a. Draw $\overline{KL}$.

   b. Plot point $(5, 8)$.

   c. Draw $\overline{LM}$.

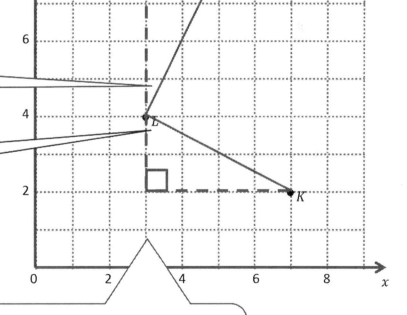

This is an acute angle, like $\angle K$, in Problem 1.

This is an acute angle, like $\angle L$, in Problem 1.

The two triangles I sketched are aligned to create a 180°, or straight angle, along the vertical grid line. So if the two acute angles of the triangles add up to 90°, the angle in between them, $\angle MLK$, must also be 90°.

Lesson 16:   Construct perpendicular line segments, and analyze relationships of the
             coordinate pairs.

33

©2015 Great Minds. eureka-math.org
G5-M1-HWH-1.3.0-07.2015

d. Explain how you know ∠MLK is a right angle without measuring it.

I used the grid lines to sketch a right triangle with side $\overline{LK}$, just like in Problem 1. Then I visualized sliding and rotating the triangle so side $\overline{LK}$ matched up with side $\overline{LM}$.

I know that the measures of the 2 acute angles of a right triangle add up to 90°. So when the long side of the triangle and the short side of the triangle form a straight angle, 180°, the angle in between them, ∠MLK, is also 90°.

e. Compare the coordinates of points L and K. What is the difference of the x-coordinates? The y-coordinates?

L (3,4) and K (7,2)

The difference of the x-coordinates is 4.

The difference of the y-coordinates is 2.

f. Compare the coordinates of points L and M. What is the difference of the x-coordinates? The y-coordinates?

L (3,4) and M (5,8)

The difference of the x-coordinates is 2.

The difference of the y-coordinates is 4.

g. What is the relationship of the differences you found in parts (e) and (f) to the triangles of which these two segments are a part?

The difference in the value of the coordinates is either 2 or 4. That makes sense to me because the triangles that these two segments are part of have a height of either 2 or 4 and a base of either 2 or 4.

When I visualize the triangle sliding and rotating, it makes sense that the x-coordinates and y-coordinates will change by a value of 2 or 4 because that's the length of the triangle's height and base.

Lesson 16:   Construct perpendicular line segments, and analyze relationships of the coordinate pairs.

EUREKA MATH

©2015 Great Minds. eureka-math.org
G5-M1-HWH-1.3.0-07.2015

G5-M6-Lesson 17

> In order to create a figure that is symmetric about $\overleftrightarrow{UR}$, I need to find points that are drawn using a line *perpendicular to* and *equidistant from* (the same distance from) the line of symmetry, $\overleftrightarrow{UR}$.

1. Draw to create a figure that is symmetric about $\overleftrightarrow{UR}$.

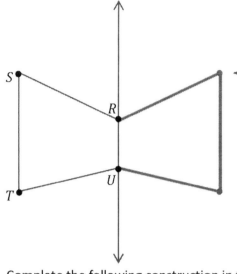

> The distance from this point to the line of symmetry is the same as the distance from the line of symmetry to point S, when measured on a line perpendicular to the line of symmetry.

2. Complete the following construction in the space below.

    a. Plot 3 non-collinear points, A, B, and C.

> I know that collinear means that the points are "lying on the same straight line," so non-collinear must mean that the three points are *not* on the same straight line.

    b. Draw $\overline{AB}$, $\overline{BC}$, and $\overleftrightarrow{AC}$.

    c. Plot point D, and draw the remaining sides, such that quadrilateral $ABCD$ is symmetric about $\overleftrightarrow{AC}$.

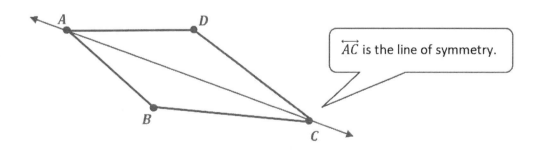

> $\overleftrightarrow{AC}$ is the line of symmetry.

G5-M6-Lesson 18

Use the plane to the right to complete the following tasks.

This will be a vertical line.

a. Draw a line h whose rule is x is always 7.

b. Plot the points from Table A on the grid in order. Then, draw line segments to connect the points in order.

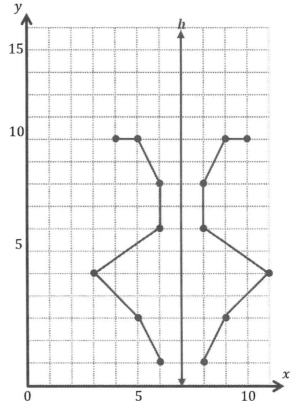

Table A

(x, y)
$(6, 1)$
$(5, 3)$
$(3, 5)$
$(6, 7)$
$(6, 9)$
$(5, 11)$
$(4, 11)$

Table B

(x, y)
$(8, 1)$
$(9, 3)$
$(11, 5)$
$(8, 7)$
$(8, 9)$
$(9, 11)$
$(10, 11)$

c. Complete the drawing to create a figure that is symmetric about line h. For each point in Table A, record the symmetric point on the other side of h.

d. Compare the y-coordinates in Table A with those in Table B. What do you notice?

The y-coordinates in Table A are the same as in Table B. Because the line of symmetry is a vertical line, only the x-coordinates will change.

e. Compare the x-coordinates in Table A with those in Table B. What do you notice?

I notice that the difference in the x-coordinates is always an even number because the distance that a point is from line h has to double.

©2015 Great Minds. eureka-math.org
G5-M1-HWH-1.3.0-07.2015

G5-M6-Lesson 19

The line graph below tracks the balance of Sheldon's checking account at the end of each day between June 10 and June 24. Use the information in the graph to answer the questions that follow.

> I know that it is important to read the scale on the vertical axis so that I know what units the data is referring to. In this graph, the 1 means $1,000, and the 2 means $2,000. I can tell that each grid line skip-counts by $250.

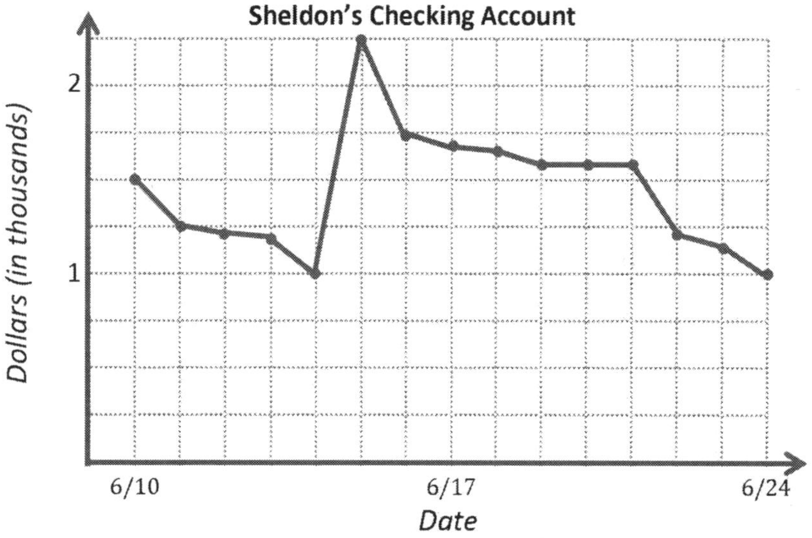

Sheldon's Checking Account

Dollars (in thousands)

Date

a. About how much money does Sheldon have in his checking account on June 10?

   Sheldon has $1,500 in his account on June 10. I can tell because the point is on the line exactly between $1,000 and $2,000.

b. If Sheldon spends $250 from his checking account on June 24, about how much money will he have left in his account?

   Sheldon will have $750 left. ← $1,000 − $250 = $750

c. Sheldon received a payment from his job that went directly into his checking account. On which day did this most likely occur? Explain how you know.

   The amount of money in his account increased by $1,250 on June 15. This is most likely the day he was paid by his job.

d. Sheldon paid rent for his apartment during the time shown in the graph. On which day did this most likely occur? Explain how you know.

   Sheldon might have paid his rent on either June 15 or June 21. These are the two days where Sheldon's account went down most quickly.

G5-M6-Lesson 20

Use the graph to answer the questions.

Hector left his home at 6:00 a.m. to train for a bicycle race. He used his GPS watch to keep track of the number of miles he traveled at the end of each hour of his trip. He uploaded the data to his computer, which gave him the line graph below:

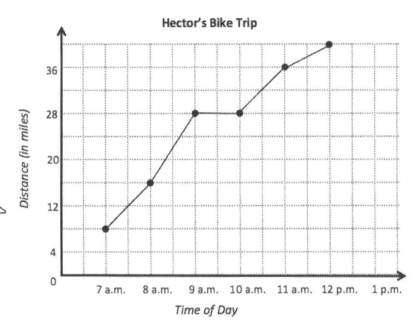

Hector's Bike Trip

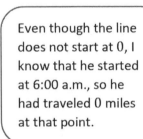

Even though the line does not start at 0, I know that he started at 6:00 a.m., so he had traveled 0 miles at that point.

a. How far did Hector travel in all? How long did it take?

Hector traveled 40 miles in 6 hours.

Hector started at 6:00 a.m. and stopped at noon. That's 6 hours.

The last data point at 12:00 p.m. shows 40 miles.

b.   Hector took a one-hour break to have a snack and take some pictures. What time did he stop? How do you know?

Hector took his break from 9 a.m. to 10 a.m. The horizontal line at this time tells me that Hector's distance did not change; therefore, he wasn't biking for that hour.

c.   During which hour did Hector ride the slowest?

Hector's slowest hour was his last one between 11:00 a.m. and noon. He only rode 4 miles in that last hour whereas in the other hours he rode at least 8 miles (except when he took his break).

I also know I can look at how steep the line is between two points to help me know how fast or slow Hector rode. The line is not very steep between 11:00 a.m and noon, so I know that was his slowest hour.

G5-M6-Lesson 21

Meyer read four times as many books as Zenin. Lenox read as many as Meyer and Zenin combined. Parks read half as many books as Zenin. In total, all four read 147 books. How many books did each child read?

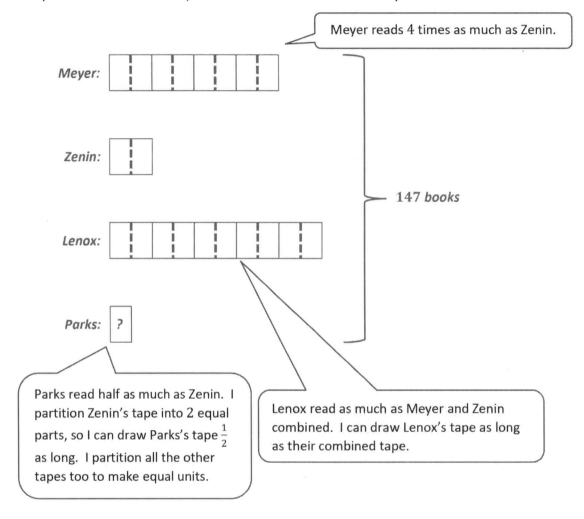

Meyer reads 4 times as much as Zenin.

147 *books*

Parks read half as much as Zenin. I partition Zenin's tape into 2 equal parts, so I can draw Parks's tape $\frac{1}{2}$ as long. I partition all the other tapes too to make equal units.

Lenox read as much as Meyer and Zenin combined. I can draw Lenox's tape as long as their combined tape.

21 *units* = 147 *books*

1 *unit* = 147 *books* ÷ 21 = 7 *books*

Parks read 7 *books*.

$7 \times 8 = 56$ Meyer read 56 *books*.

$7 \times 2 = 14$ Zenin read 14 *books*.

$56 + 14 = 70$ Lenox read 70 *books*.

Lesson 21:   Make sense of complex, multi-step problems and persevere in solving them. Share and critique peer solutions.

EUREKA MATH

G5-M6-Lesson 22

Solve using any method. Show all your thinking.

> I know that squares have all 4 sides of equal length.

Study this diagram showing all the squares. Fill in the table.

Figure	Area in Square Centimeters
1	9 cm^2
2	81 cm^2
3	36 cm^2
5	9 cm^2
6	9 cm^2

> The table says the area of Figure 1 is 9 cm^2.
> $3 \text{ cm} \times 3 \text{ cm} = 9 \text{ cm}^2$
> I know that each side of Figure 1 is 3 cm long.

> Figures 5 and 6 are the same size as Figure 1. They also have an area of 9 cm^2.

Figure 3:

$3 \text{ cm} + 3 \text{ cm} = 6 \text{ cm}$

$6 \text{ cm} \times 6 \text{ cm} = 36 \text{ cm}^2$

> Figure 3 shares a side with Figures 5 and 6. Since the side lengths of Figures 5 and 6 are 3 cm each, the side length of Figure 3 must be 6 cm.

Figure 2:

$6 \text{ cm} + 3 \text{ cm} = 9 \text{ cm}$

$9 \text{ cm} \times 9 \text{ cm} = 81 \text{ cm}^2$

> Figure 2 shares a side with Figures 3 and 5. Since the side lengths of Figures 3 and 5 are 6 cm and 3 cm, respectively, the side length of Figure 2 must be 9 cm.

EUREKA MATH   Lesson 22:   Make sense of complex, multi-step problems and persevere in solving them. Share and critique peer solutions.   41

©2015 Great Minds. eureka-math.org
G5-M1-HWH-1.3.0-07.2015

G5-M6-Lesson 23

In the diagram, the length of Figure B is $\frac{4}{7}$ the length of Figure A. Figure A has an area of 182 in^2.
Find the perimeter of the entire figure.

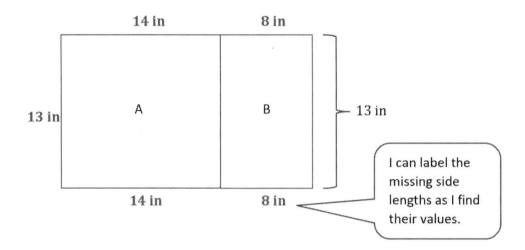

I can label the missing side lengths as I find their values.

I can find the length of Figure A by dividing the area by the width.

Now that I know the length of Figure A, I can use it to find the length of Figure B.

I can find the perimeter of the entire figure by adding up all of the sides.

Figure A:

$$\text{Area} = \text{length} \times \text{width}$$
$$182 = \underline{\quad} \times 13$$
$$182 \div 13 = 14$$

The length of Figure A is 14 inches.

Figure B:

$\frac{4}{7}$ *of* 14 *inches*

$$\frac{4}{7} \times 14$$

$$= \frac{4 \times 14}{7}$$

$$= \frac{56}{7}$$

$$= 8$$

The length of Figure B is 8 inches.

Entire Figure:

$$14 + 8 + 13 + 8 + 14 + 13 = 70$$

The perimeter of the entire figure is 70 inches.

Lesson 23:   Make sense of complex, multi-step problems and persevere in solving
them. Share and critique peer solutions.

EUREKA
MATH

G5-M6-Lesson 24

Howard's Baseball Camp welcomed 96 athletes on the first day of camp. Five-eighths of the athletes began practicing hitting. The hitting coach sent $\frac{2}{5}$ of the hitters to work on bunting. Half of the bunters were left-handed hitters. The left-handed bunters were put into teams of 2 to practice together. How many teams of 2 were practicing bunting?

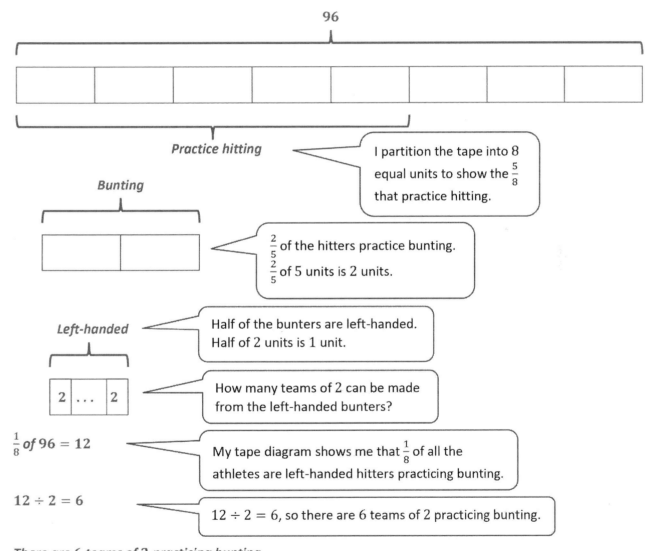

There are 6 teams of 2 practicing bunting.

Lesson 24:   Make sense of complex, multi-step problems and persevere in solving
             them. Share and critique peer solutions.   43

©2015 Great Minds. eureka-math.org
G5-M1-HWH-1.3.0-07.2015

G5-M6-Lesson 25

Jason and Selena had $96 altogether at first. After Jason spent $\frac{1}{5}$ of his money and Selena lent $15 of her money, they had the same amount of money left. How much money did each of them have at first?

> This is important. *After* Jason spends and Selena lends, *then* they have the same amount left. I need to make sure that my model shows this.

> I partition the tape representing Jason's money into 5 equal parts to show the $\frac{1}{5}$ that he spent.

spent

Jason:

$96

Selena: $15

lent

> My model shows me that 9 units, plus the $15 that Selena lent, is equal to $96.

> To show that Selena and Jason have the same amount of money left, I partition the tape representing Selena's money the same way that I did Jason's.

9 *units* + $15 = $96

9 *units* = $81

1 *unit* = $81 ÷ 9 = $9

> Now that I know the value of 1 unit, I can find out how much money they each had at first.

Jason:

1 *unit* = $9

5 *units* = 5 × $9 = $45

Jason had $45 at first.

Selena:

1 *unit* = $9

4 *units* = 4 × $9 = $36

$36 + $15 = $51

Selena had $51 at first.

Lesson 25:   Make sense of complex, multi-step problems and persevere in solving them. Share and critique peer solutions.   **EUREKA MATH**

G5-M6-Lesson 26

1. For the phrase below, write a numerical expression, and then evaluate your expression.

   Subtract three halves from one sixth of forty-two.

   $\frac{1}{6} \times 42 - \frac{3}{2}$

   > Even though it says the word *"subtract"* first, I need to have something to subtract from. So I won't subtract until I find the value of *"one sixth of forty-two."*

   $= \frac{42}{6} - \frac{3}{2}$

   $= 7 - \frac{3}{2}$

   $= 7 - 1\frac{1}{2}$

   $= 5\frac{1}{2}$

2. Write at least 2 numerical expressions for the phrase below. Then, solve.

   Two fifths of nine

   $\frac{2}{5} \times 9$ $\left(\frac{1}{5} \times 9\right) \times 2$

   $\frac{2}{5} \times 9$

   > This is *"one fifth of nine, doubled,"* which is equal to *"two fifths of nine."*

   $= \frac{2 \times 9}{5}$

   $= \frac{18}{5}$

   > *"Two fifths of nine"* is equal to $3\frac{3}{5}$.

   $= 3\frac{3}{5}$

3. Use $<$, $>$, or $=$ to make true number sentences without calculating. Explain your thinking.

a. $\left(481 \times \frac{9}{16}\right) \times \frac{2}{10}$ $\left(481 \times \frac{9}{16}\right) \times \frac{7}{10}$

   Both expressions have the same first factor, $\left(481 \times \frac{9}{16}\right)$.

   Since the second factor, $\frac{7}{10}$, *is greater than* $\frac{2}{10}$, *the expression on the right is greater.*

b. $\left(4 \times \frac{1}{10}\right) + \left(9 \times \frac{1}{100}\right)$ $\boxed{>}$ 0.409

   The expression on the left is equal to 0.49.

   The expression on the right also has 0 *ones and* 4 *tenths, but there are* 0 *hundredths in* 0.409.

EUREKA
MATH

G5-M6-Lesson 27

1. Use the RDW process to solve the word problem below.

Daquan brought 32 cupcakes to school. Of those cupcakes, $\frac{3}{4}$ were chocolate, and the rest were vanilla. Daquan's classmates ate $\frac{5}{8}$ of the chocolate cupcakes and $\frac{3}{4}$ of the vanilla. How many cupcakes are left?

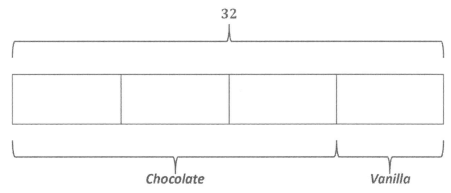

Chocolate

(of which $\frac{5}{8}$ are eaten)

Of all the cupcakes, 24 are chocolate.

Vanilla

(of which $\frac{3}{4}$ are eaten)

Of all the cupcakes, 8 are vanilla.

Chocolate eaten:

$\frac{3}{4}$ of $32 = \frac{3 \times 32}{4} = \frac{96}{4} = 24$

$\frac{5}{8}$ of $24 = \frac{5 \times 24}{8} = \frac{120}{8} = 15$

Of the 24 chocolate cupcakes, 15 were eaten.

15 chocolate cupcakes were eaten.

Vanilla eaten:

$\frac{1}{4}$ of $32 = \frac{1 \times 32}{4} = \frac{32}{4} = 8$

$\frac{3}{4}$ of $8 = \frac{3 \times 8}{4} = \frac{24}{4} = 6$

Of the 8 vanilla cupcakes, 6 were eaten.

6 vanilla cupcakes were eaten.

Cupcakes left:

$32 - (15 + 6) = 32 - 21 = 11$

I find the number of leftover cupcakes by subtracting those that were eaten from the 32 original cupcakes.

11 cupcakes are left.

2. Write and solve a word problem for the expression in the chart below.

Expression	Word Problem	Solution
$5 - \left(\dfrac{5}{12} + \dfrac{1}{3}\right)$	*During her 5-day work week, Mrs. Gomez spends $\dfrac{5}{12}$ of one day and $\dfrac{1}{3}$ of another in meetings. How much of her work week is* <u>not</u> *spent in meetings?*	$5 - \left(\dfrac{5}{12} + \dfrac{1}{3}\right)$ $= 5 - \left(\dfrac{5}{12} + \dfrac{4}{12}\right)$ $= 5 - \dfrac{9}{12}$ $= 4\dfrac{3}{12}$ $= 4\dfrac{1}{4}$ *$4\dfrac{1}{4}$ days of Mrs. Gomez' work week was not spent in meetings.*

©2015 Great Minds. eureka-math.org
G5-M1-HWH-1.3.0-07.2015

G5-M6-Lesson 29

Use your ruler, protractor, and set square to help you give as many names as possible for each figure below. Then, explain your reasoning for how you named each figure.

Figure	Names	Reasoning for Names
a.	quadrilateral trapezoid	*This figure is a <u>quadrilateral</u> because it is a closed figure with 4 sides.* *It's also a <u>trapezoid</u> because it has at least one pair of parallel sides. The top and bottom sides are parallel.*
b. I use my protractor and ruler to measure the angles and the side lengths. This shape has four 90° angles and four equal sides. That means it's a square, but it has other names, too.	quadrilateral trapezoid parallelogram rectangle rhombus kite square	*This figure is a <u>quadrilateral</u> because it is a closed figure with 4 sides.* *It's also a <u>trapezoid</u> because it has at least one pair of parallel sides. This shape actually has 2 pairs.* *This shape is also a <u>parallelogram</u> because opposite sides are both parallel and equal in length.* *It's also a <u>rectangle</u> because it has 4 right angles.* *It's a <u>rhombus</u> because all 4 sides are equal in length.* *It's also a <u>kite</u> because it has 2 pairs of adjacent sides that are equal in length.* *But most specifically, it's a <u>square</u> because it has 4 right angles and 4 sides of equal length.*

©2015 Great Minds. eureka-math.org
G5-M1-HWH-1.3.0-07.2015

G5-M6-Lesson 31

Lesson Notes

To get a better understanding of the Fibonacci numbers, watch the short video, "Doodling in Math: Spirals, Fibonacci, and Being a Plant" by Vi Hart (http://youtu.be/ahXIMUkSXX0).

1. In your own words, describe what you know about the Fibonacci numbers.

    The Fibonacci numbers are really interesting. They're a list of numbers. You can always find the next number in the series by adding together the 2 numbers that come before it.

    For example, if part of the series is 13 and then 21, then the next number in the list will be 34 because 13 + 21 = 34.

    I can remember the first few Fibonacci numbers:

    $$1, 1, 2, 3, 5, 8, 13, 21, 34.$$

2. Describe what the drawing you did in class today looked like.

    I can visualize what we drew in class. It looked like this:

    At first, the drawing just looked like a bunch of square boxes drawn near one another that had a side in common. But then we drew a diagonal line across each square. Then we drew a more curved line inside each square, and it created this really neat spiral pattern, kind of like a seashell.

    After we drew it, we wrote down the side length of each square we drew and realized that they were the Fibonacci numbers. In other words, the first 2 squares we drew had a side length of 1, then the next square had a side length of 2, then 3, then 5, and so on.

G5-M6-Lesson 32

Lesson Notes

To get a better understanding of the Fibonacci numbers, watch the short video, "Doodling in Math: Spirals, Fibonacci, and Being a Plant" by Vi Hart (http://youtu.be/ahXIMUkSXX0).

1. Complete the Fibonacci sequence in the table below.

The values in the top row tell the order of the numbers in the sequence. For example, this is the 6th number in the sequence.

1	2	3	4	5	6	7	8	9
1	1	2	3	5	8	13	21	34

I can find the value of the next number in the sequence by adding together the two previous numbers. $5 + 8 = 13$; therefore, the 7th number in the sequence is 13.

2. If the 12th and 13th numbers in the sequence are 144 and 233, respectively, what is the 11th number in the series?

_____ $+ 144 = 233$

$233 - 144 = 89$ What number plus 144 is equal to 233? I can use subtraction to solve.

The 11th number in the series is 89.

G5-M6-Lesson 33

Find a rectangular box at your home. Use a ruler to measure the dimensions of the box to the nearest centimeter. Then, calculate the volume of the box.

> I find the volume of rectangular prisms, or boxes, by multiplying the 3 dimensions together.
> Volume = length × width × height

Item	Length	Width	Height	Volume
Toy Shoe Box	8 cm	3 cm	6 cm	144 cm^3

> The length of the shoe box was exactly 7.5 cm, but the directions said to measure to the nearest centimeter. I round 7.5 up to 8.

> $8 \times 3 \times 6 = 24 \times 6 = 144$
> The volume of the shoe box is 144 cubic centimeters.

©2015 Great Minds. eureka-math.org
G5-M1-HWH-1.3.0-07.2015